SPIRIT OF HAMBLE
FOLLAND AIRCRAFT

Sydney Lodge was designed by the eminent architect Sir John Soane and built between 1789 and 1798 as a private residence. It remained as this until 1935. A Grade II Listed building, it now houses Hamble Group's Conference and Administrative Centre.

SPIRIT OF HAMBLE
FOLLAND AIRCRAFT

Derek N. James

TEMPUS

First published 2000, Reprinted 2003
Copyright © Derek N. James, 2000

Tempus Publishing Limited
The Mill, Brimscombe Port,
Stroud, Gloucestershire, GL5 2QG
www.tempus-publishing.com

ISBN 0 7524 2102 6

Typesetting and origination by
Tempus Publishing Limited
Printed in Great Britain by
Midway Clark Printing, Wiltshire

Gnat T1s of the RAF Central Flying School.

Contents

Foreword

From Fabric and Wood to Titanium and Carbon Fibre

No engineering activity has seen more drastic change in its short existence than Aerospace. The advances in propulsion and electronics are there to be seen and in structures – Hambles' speciality – fabric, string and wood have given way to complex super alloys and composite materials, all of which reconcile the seemingly conflicting requirements of lightness of weight and great strength.

These rapid developments have been the Industry's response to the constant demands of the market which, in one generation, have given rise to vast improvements in payloads, speeds, standards of comfort, safety and economics.

Hamble has kept pace with all of these developments in its sixty-five years of existence – itself a remarkable achievement. This proven ability to respond and adapt to the requirements of challenging customers provides the assurance of continued success for the Hamble team well into the twenty-first century.

Colin Chandler

Sir Colin Chandler
Former Managing Director, BAe Kingston – Brough Division
Chairman and Chief Executive, Vickers plc
Currently Chairman, Racal Electronics plc

One

The Heritage

Originally named Brown's Field, it became a small grass aerodrome in 1913 when the Admiralty began using it for visitors to a Royal Naval Air Station who arrived in aircraft with wheels rather than floats. From this field they were ferried across the Water to the Station. Two years later Fairey Aviation rented two sheds on the River bank, and test flew floatplanes there. Alliott Verdon Roe moved the design and experimental flight departments of his Manchester-based Avro company to this 'green field' site and it was here that the British Marine Aircraft Co. occupied a newly-built factory. So – where were they located? They were all at Hamble, or to use its proper name, Hamble-le-Rice, in Hampshire. The Naval Air Station was Calshot across Southampton Water.

This comparatively modest-sized peninsula, bounded by the Hamble River and Southampton Water, originally contained three separate airfields, all cheek-by-jowl with each other. Between 1913 and 1984, six aircraft manufacturers occupied factories at Hamble and no less than eleven civil or military flying and engineering training organisations were based here. Countless fighters and bombers, flying boats and airliners, floatplanes and trainers have been built, assembled, serviced or first got airborne here, and hundreds of pupils have 'Hamble' in their log-books as the place from where they made their first nail-biting solo flights or cross-country navigation exercises.

This is just a part of the Hamble Heritage. It is against this richly aviation-inspired background that, today, the Hamble Group carries on this tradition by applying its long experience and engineering expertise to the creation of advanced technology aero-structures for the world's leading aircraft and aero-engine manufacturers.

While aviation didn't arrive at Hamble until 1913, this magnificent site has always enjoyed free access to fresh and salt water with magnificent views in all directions. Thus, it is no surprise to discover that its maritime connections, which link it to the present day, stretch much further back in local history.

Between 1789 and 1798, a mansion to be named Sydney Lodge was being built on this fifty-eight acre site for the Hon. Agneta Yorke, widow of the Rt Hon. Charles Yorke, whose son, Joseph, became an Admiral. He was the first of four generations of men of the Yorke family who attained very high rank in the Royal Navy and whose families occupied Sydney Lodge until 1909. For the next twenty years it was let on short leases; then South African businessman Major Charles Goldman bought it, only to sell it when times got hard in 1936. The next buyer, British Marine Aircraft Ltd. (BMA), renewed the maritime connection. Sydney Lodge had also joined the aviation business.

Formed in February 1936 with an authorized capital of £500,000, BMA had a number of distinguished people on its Board of Directors – as will be revealed in a moment. It is difficult to understand the rationale behind the formation of British Marine Aircraft, which, as its title indicates, was to be dedicated to the production of this class of aeroplane. Not that it had a design of its own which it was bursting to turn into hardware. At a cost of some £130,000 it had acquired a licence from the Sikorsky Manufacturing Corporation of Long Island, New York, USA to build its S42-A four-engine flying boat and to sell it within the British Empire, excluding Canada. With this aeroplane it planned to tap into what the BMA Board believed would be a huge market for commercial flying boats. But there were already four established British flying boat manufacturers: Blackburn at Brough, Yorkshire, Saunders-Roe at Cowes, Isle of Wight, Short Brothers at Rochester, Kent and Supermarine just up the road (or should that be 'just up the Water') at Southampton. Shorts had just launched its great family of C-Class four-engined 'boats which would remain in service for the next fifteen years. That the market was too small to support all this production capacity was proven by the late 1930s when Blackburn and Supermarine had given up building commercial flying boats, leaving Shorts and Saunders-Roe to continue producing mainly military types.

At Hamble, BMA built a new slipway down to Southampton Water and on 11 July 1936 a huge new building was completed. It had a 200ft unobstructed-span central bay, which was 250ft long, with access through what was then the world's largest 'up-and-over' door. In this huge building 'three flying boats could be assembled at once' according to BMA's publicity. One wonders whether the use of the word 'assembled' rather than 'manufactured' was a Freudian slip and indicated that BMA intended only to assemble Sikorsky-built components rather than design and build flying boats from scratch. In any event, BMA also announced that 80ft wide machine shops, stores and other facilities would run alongside the full length of this building. Apart from this large factory building, BMA was also erecting houses for potential new employees brought in from other regions.

Unfortunately, getting hold of the components from Sikorsky for the first S42-A was proving difficult and time-consuming. Then it was discovered that the Sikorsky company was pulling out of the flying boat business to concentrate on helicopters. Supplying British Marine Aircraft with components was probably the last thing on their collective minds at Long Island. But there were more problems ahead for BMA. Britain's aircraft industry was gearing up to meet the demands of the RAF expansion plans and skilled employees were being snapped up by the established manufacturers. BMA was facing the twin problems of lack of materials and of a suitable workforce.

Although work began on the first Sikorsky S42-A, optimistically designated the BM1 and registered G-AEGZ, it was never completed. Thus, by early 1937, British Marine Aircraft had made a loss of some £222,000 and half an aeroplane. There was just one glimmer of hope flickering some 100 miles west of Hamble in Somerset.

At that time there were rumours that Westland Aircraft Co. would take over the BMA factory at Hamble instead of expanding its Yeovil factory. For possibly the first time, the older members of the Petter family's grip on Westland Aircraft was publicly contested. This was when Peter Acland, Westland's joint managing director, and W.E.W. 'Teddy' Petter opposed Sir Ernest Petter's proposal to merge with BMA in order to gain additional production facilities. British Marine's authorized capital was substantial and its Board members had impressive pedigrees. Air Marshal Sir John Higgins was a director of Airports Ltd; Admiral Henry Grant was a director of Cable & Wireless Ltd; Lord Willoughby de Broke was chairman of British Aircraft Manufacturing Co. Ltd; Charles Best was its Managing Director and George Handasyde was a member of its Board; William Craven-Ellis was a director of Aircraft Industries Corporation Ltd and Brigadier-General Guy Lubbock was on the Board of Bankers Investment Trust Ltd. British Marine's top brass really glittered.

At a Westland shareholders' meeting convened to increase the company's capital to £750,000 by creation of one million five-shilling shares, Acland proposed to adjourn on the grounds that British Marine Aircraft had an agreement with British Aircraft Manufacturing Co. through which the latter got an annual £5,000 management fee for four years (this provided support during British Marine's early years of operation) and which was unacceptable to the majority of Westland shareholders. Sir Ernest Petter admitted that this 'unfortunate circumstance had arisen causing a difference of opinion'; however, he explained that British Aircraft Manufacturing would waive this agreement and he would therefore be against the proposed adjournment which had been seconded by his son Teddy Petter! On a vote lost by nine votes to ten, the Westland Board decided not to take over British Marine Aircraft.

When the Westland acquisition failed to materialize the bottom fell out of the BMA Board's lifeboat. It then believed that the only course left open to it was to liquidate; however, in 1937 a shareholders' committee secured a halt to negotiations and managed to replace the entire BMA Board with new members. This was an equally glittering assemblage. Chairman was thirty-five-year old Alan Paul Good, a Lincoln's Inn solicitor turned entrepreneur. He was an astute financier and chairman of Heenan and Froude, and of Lagonda Motors which he had rescued from the hands of the Receivers, plus a number of small diesel engine companies. Edgar Granville was chairman of the first British Airways; Captain J. Dawson Paul, a director of Boulton & Paul Ltd; Alfred Kimpton was a delegate director of several ICI subsidiaries and Henry Philip Folland, formerly Gloster Aircraft Company's chief designer, who had been appointed technical director of British Marine Aircraft.

The appointment of Folland was of great significance to BMA. During his later years with Gloster Aircraft Co. he had become frustrated and dispirited at his apparent inability to design a contract-winning aeroplane. Following the Hawker Aircraft takeover of the Gloster company in 1934, Folland had found it impossible to accept subordination under Sydney Camm, Hawker's chief designer. Hugh Burroughes, a founding director of the Gloster company, told the author 'Folland had produced some fine aircraft for Gloster, particularly the Gamecock, Gauntlet and Gladiator and a family of racing floatplanes for the Schneider Trophy Contests. Before that, while he was at the Royal Aircraft Factory at Farnborough, he had designed the SE.5 and SE.5A, the latter regarded by many pilots as the best Allied single-seat fighter of the First World War. After Gloster was taken over he thought that the new owner would give preference to designs by Camm whose Furies, Harts and Demons had put him in the top rank of designers. Folland had been accused of being unimaginative but he was one of the most outstanding designers of his era'. Because of this mental turmoil Henry Folland resigned from Gloster Aircraft in 1937 and joined BMA at Hamble. With him he took several of his design team, including his assistant, little Henry Preston, and Frank Radcliffe.

The new BMA Board's prime task was to reverse the Company's losses during its first trading year. At the second Annual General Meeting, on 10 December 1937, it reported that progress was being made with the re-organisation of the Company. The chairman, Allan Good, who was an imposing figure, 6ft 5in tall and weighing some 20 stones, said 'When we took over, the Number One Unit of your factory was inhabited by a limited number of workmen and the derelict remains of a Sikorsky flying boat which had barely been commenced. Number Two Unit was entirely vacant. Today, Number One Unit is actively engaged on sub-contract work and Number Two Unit is partly so engaged'. He went on to report that several Imperial Airways C-Class Empire flying boats were being overhauled in the big factory. 'Although this work is being carried out by Imperial Airways staff', he said 'we are doing a certain amount of work for them and I hope that this work will increase'. He could have had little idea of just how his hopes for this sub-contract work would be realized and would set the pattern for BMA and its successors at Hamble.

A decision of major importance was taken at a subsequent Extraordinary General Meeting. This was to change the Company's name to Folland Aircraft Ltd. The Board believed that it would be an advantage to link the name of the Company to the man who was now its managing director. He was well known, and trusted by the Air Ministry and foreign Governments as a successful designer over the previous twenty-five years. The new name was officially approved by the Board of Trade on 23 December 1937.

An aerial view of the Hamble-le-Rice site where British Marine Aircraft built its factory in 1935. The aircraft are Avro Cadets. Two belonged to Hamble-based Air Service Training and the inverted leader was Avro's own aeroplane.

British Marine Aircraft bought Cliff House and grounds to ensure access to Southampton Water via a new slipway. It was used by Folland Aircraft's Sports and Social Club, then became the Apprentice Training School before being sold in the late 1980s for private development.

The Sikorsky S-42 flying boat first flew on 29 March 1934 at Long Island. The type was to have been licence-built by British Marine Aircraft at Hamble.

A Sikorsky S-42 flying boat on Vickers Supermarine Aviation's slipway in 1937.

A Short S23 Empire flying boat undergoing routine maintenance in British Marine Aircraft's main hangar during 1937. Named *Cambria* and registered G-ADUV its 114ft span wing fits easily into this giant building.

Ceres, the seventeenth Short Empire flying boat, first flew on 16 July 1937. It is seen on the slipway in front of Cliff House.

Two

Folland Aircraft Ltd

Folland Aircraft quickly got to grips with obtaining sub-contract orders from the major aircraft manufacturers and expanding its work force. During 1938 the number of employees rose from 180 to 500 and the Air Ministry invited the Company to tender for two new designs, one of which was a large civil airliner. At the Annual General Meeting that year Alan Good announced that sub-contract work had grown by some 260 per cent. With considerable forethought the factory was also being expanded to meet wartime production programmes. Folland Aircraft's expertise and very high standards of workmanship were to ensure full employment for many years. During the last week of January 1939 Sir Kingsley Wood, Secretary of State for Air, came to Folland Aircraft as part of his series of fact-finding visits to every British aircraft manufacturer. He told Folland that he '…was impressed by the efficient way in which the Company had got down to sub-contract work'.

When the Second World War began Bristol Aeroplane Co. soon provided sub-contract work at Hamble with orders for Blenheim and Beaufort nose sections. This was followed by sub-assemblies for the Beaufighter. A major programme was the production of wings for the Supermarine Seafire, plus more than 3,500 Spitfire ailerons for these renowned fighters. For the Vickers Wellington and Warwick bombers Folland produced 2,800 engine nacelles and 5,299 bomb beams. In addition sixty Hurricanes were modified for use as catapult-launched fighters on merchant ships. Short Brothers placed orders for components for its Sunderland flying boat and large-scale production of sub-assemblies for the de Havilland Mosquito and Hornet was also undertaken.

But it was not all sub-contract work at Folland. With a renowned aircraft designer heading the Company the small design team was soon producing projects with designations beginning at Fo100. Few details of this first Folland project exist, but it is known to have been a four-engine bomber with Rolls-Royce Vulture engines. The Fo108 of 1940 was designed to meet the unusual Air Ministry Specification 43/37 which called only for an engine-less airframe. This was because the requirement was for a flying test bed aircraft able to accommodate a range of engines of different configurations. Three companies were invited to tender for this contract: Percival Aircraft, General Aircraft and Folland. The Folland Fo108 won and in 1938 was awarded a contract by the Directorate of Technical Development for twelve aircraft to be serialled P1774-1785.

Designed with a standard all-metal monocoque fuselage aft of the engine bulkhead and mountings, the F43/37 had a sub-frame attached to the main engine bearers so that as the weights of the different engines being tested were different, this sub-frame could be lengthened to maintain the same centre of gravity. The wings were principally wooden and built in one piece. The structure consisted of two spruce-ply box spars and girder-type ribs clad with a spruce skin, the section between the spars being carried through the fuselage. The leading edge slats and the ailerons were wooden but the flaps were entirely of light-alloy construction. Wood was used for the tail unit construction. The wide-track fixed and spatted main landing gear units were attached and strut-braced to the wing spars. Although single-engined, it was a large aeroplane with a 58ft wingspan, and standing nearly 17ft tall.

Soon after war began Folland Aircraft was instructed to disperse its production facilities because it was so near to Southampton. Apart from occupying some local premises Henry Folland found sites in his old home town, Cheltenham. Here a large garage and a bus depot were taken over for the Fo108 and other aircraft components. The first two aircraft were, in fact, assembled at Eastleigh – which was nearer to Southampton than Hamble – and flown to Staverton near Gloucester in late 1940. As Folland Aircraft didn't have a test pilot, Gloster Aircraft Co. allowed its chief test pilot Gerry Sayer and his deputy Neil Daunt (who was always known as Michael) to do the test flying.

Both pilots flew these aeroplanes but didn't like them very much. Sayer was quite reluctant to criticise their handling characteristics but Daunt was more forthcoming. He once told the author; 'They were frightful aeroplanes with no stability. Bloody dangerous to fly'. In fact it was he who dubbed them the 'Folland Frightful', a name which has stuck throughout the years. During a subsequent programme of dives with one of these aeroplanes, the speed being increased dive by dive, its tail broke off. Daunt, who was flying it, was hurled through the canopy but somehow managed to pull his parachute ripcord – and remembered nothing more until he came to on the ground having broken his collarbone and a wrist. The first person to find him was a local vicar. Daunt, who was still semi-conscious, hit the poor man and swore at him!

Engines test-flown in this unusual aircraft were the Bristol Hercules and Centaurus air-cooled radials and the Napier Sabre and Rolls-Royce Griffon in-line, liquid-cooled engines. Some sources record that the aircraft could also accept the Armstrong Siddeley Deerhound radial, Rolls-Royce's liquid-cooled, in-line Merlin and X-configuration Vulture and the unusual Exe and Pennine which were air-cooled X-configuration engines; however, there is no evidence of these engines being installed. During one five-month period five Folland 43/37s crashed – two on 14 September 1944 – of which four were testing the Centaurus and the other a Sabre. While Michael Daunt, clearly, was not happy about flying this big aeroplane, the flight observers liked it. Harold Parkin had this to say about it. 'I recall the Folland Fo108 as being an ideal flying test bed in a number of respects, in particular from the ground engineers' and flight observers' standpoint. There was always room to work and install test equipment whether it was within the areas of the engine nacelle or the airframe'. Two Fo108s were retired in March 1945; another at de Havilland's Hatfield factory was still in evidence in 1947 and Napier also had one for many years after the war.

The Norwegian Campaign during the spring of 1940 underlined the urgent need for a floatplane fighter able to operate from sheltered waters. By the time Folland Aircraft had fitted two Spitfires with floats from a Blackburn Roc the campaign had been lost. However, two years later, following a requirement for such an aircraft for operations from secret Middle East locations, Folland received a contract for twelve Spitfire floatplane conversion kits and the assembly of two Spitfire Mk Vbs to full floatplane standards. This involved fitting a re-styled tail unit with a ventral fin to counter the additional side area of the floats, mounting a tropical radiator in a position where it wouldn't swallow spray from the twin-float alighting gear, and using a four-bladed propeller in place of the earlier three-bladed unit. Trials were begun from Southampton Water but were moved to Saunders-Roe's base at Beaumaris on Anglesey after they had been fired on by local anti-aircraft batteries! However, on test flights the performance was reduced, the Spitfire's two big 'boots' knocking 30mph off the top speed. Again, the speed of advance of enemy forces brought the campaign in the Dodecanese islands to a halt and the project was abandoned. Nevertheless, six float conversion sets were sent to the Middle East and three aircraft were used out of Alexandria, Egypt.

Specification S15/39 covered the requirements for an experimental multi-role torpedo reconnaissance bomber; however, it was succeeded by Specification E28/40, issued in February 1941 and intended as a replacement for the ungainly Fairey Barracuda. There were doubts about the availability of several of the engines specified with a Rolls-Royce Griffon, Napier Sabre and Bristol Centaurus being called for at different stages. The maximum scantlings were set down in the Specification: wings to span 52ft 5in but not an inch over 18ft when folded for snug parking in an aircraft carrier's below-decks hangar. It had to be 44ft nose to tail and stand no taller than 13ft 6in. A maximum all-up weight of 20,000lb and a 200 knot cruise speed when carrying a torpedo were specified. The Folland Fo116 project to meet this requirement was a monoplane with high-lift shoulder wings whose incidence could be varied from 4 degrees to 15 degrees in flight. The wings had large area-increasing flaps moving in four prominent external guides. A dorsal gun-turret was mounted on the rear fuselage but, strangely, a fixed landing gear was proposed. A contract was received by Folland in January 1941 and serial number DX160 was allocated to the prototype. Production began at one of the Cheltenham dispersal factories but work was stopped late in 1942 because of the urgency of work on the Fo117 advanced cannon-armed fighter project with a Centaurus XII engine designed to meet Specification F6/42. Here it was in competition with the Hawker Tempest and a Westland project, but was not successful.

This design was modified and, in December 1943, as the Fo118, it was submitted to meet Specification F19/43. An alternative design to F19/43 indicates that it had a mixed propulsion system using both a 2,500hp Centaurus engine plus an unspecified turbo-jet engine. A design feature of this project was the use of a one-piece wing from tip-to-tip which Folland had proposed for use in the Gloster F5/34 radial-engined, single-seat fighter before he left Gloster Aircraft Co. Had the Fo117 been accepted, production would have been handed over to English Electric's Aviation Division at Warton, Lancs.

Throughout the early war years the Folland production floor area was being regularly increased at the main factory and at several dispersal sites in Woolston, Eastleigh, and Southampton. By 1943 the Company owned or controlled no less than 500,000 square feet of floor space.

When Henry Folland had joined the Gloucestershire Aircraft Co. (GAC) on 1 August 1921, one of that company's directors was A.W. Martyn. His own company, H.H. Martyn Ltd, had formed an aircraft department during the First World War which became the GAC. A.W. Martyn had soon launched an apprenticeship scheme in this new company, something which was much admired by Folland. When he left GAC (now renamed Gloster Aircraft Company) and joined British Marine Aircraft he took with him the seed of an idea to initiate a similar scheme at Hamble. This he did during the Second World War and continued to take a close interest in it and the apprentices throughout his life at Hamble.

In mid-1944 Folland Aircraft was building components for two twin-engine Bristol aeroplanes; these were the Buckingham bomber and the Brigand torpedo fighter. Just a year later aircraft work accounted for only about 25 per cent of new orders and the number of employees had diminished by nearly one-third. By 1946 the pace of change in this volatile industry had caused a 180 degree turn-about in the Company's work. Wisely, the Company gradually diversified its interests, making the Divan-Robe, a combined bed and wardrobe, the Pony, a light electric industrial truck, plus refrigerators and aluminium, pre-fabricated houses. Then there were the Folland Tool Box and Vincent HRD motorcycle components. All helped to keep the wolf from the hangar door.

But aviation sub-contract work was never very far over the horizon and soon the names Viking, Dove, Vampire, Sea Vampire and Brabazon were on everyone's lips at Hamble. Folland Aircraft not only designed and produced all of the Brabazon's huge control surfaces but also all its ground handling and servicing equipment. These were to be followed by the Comet and Britannia civil transport aircraft and the military Canberra, Venom and Sea Vixen. Even wings of the little de Havilland Chipmunk two-seat sport and basic trainer aircraft could be seen in the Folland factory. The project office was still busy. From it came the Fo126 for an air-sea rescue amphibian having swept wings high on the hull, a vee tail unit and a pusher engine turning contra-rotating propellers mounted on the wing. Then there was the Folland F127 Fiona, a private venture, eight-passenger, high-wing monoplane with one Gipsy Major 10 engine in the nose and two more as pusher engines in the wings. Responding to Specification X30/46 for a medium glider for the Airborne Forces, the Folland Fo128 was a high wing, all-metal monoplane with a 'pod-and-boom' fuselage and triple fin tail unit, and an alternative wooden glider, the Fo131. Sadly, none of these innovative designs left the drawing board .

As the company sought non-aviation work, in September 1948 a Bristol Brigand TF.1 was delivered to Folland's factory for modification to a test vehicle for the Royal Navy's steam catapult and arrester gear development programme at the Royal Aircraft Establishment (RAE) at Farnborough, Hants. Folland was responsible for installing an arrester hook system in the big Brigand. This involved designing and manufacturing fuselage strong-points for the hook and catapult attachments, reinforcing the fuselage skin and replacing the inner fuel tanks with water-ballast tanks for slosh tests. This work was completed in 1949 and the aircraft was returned by road to Farnborough for re-assembly. After the trials it went back to Bristol Aeroplane Co. at Filton, Glos.

In July 1951 there was a major change in the Company hierarchy. Severe ill health had prompted the early retirement of Henry Folland, then aged sixty-two. However, although he was unable to take much part in the company's affairs, he remained on the Board until his death on 4 September 1954. He had been succeeded as managing director by forty-one-year old William Edward Willoughby Petter who had joined the Company as Folland's deputy during 1950.

Edward 'Teddy' Petter was the son of Sir Ernest Petter who had been chairman of Petters Ltd, the great diesel engine company, and of Westland Aircraft Ltd in Yeovil, which attempted to take over British Marine Aircraft back in 1937. A Cambridge graduate, he joined Westland working in the factory for a period before moving into the drawing office in 1931. Harald Penrose, Westland's chief test pilot, described young Edward Petter as 'sensitive, of logical mind, tall and poetic in appearance and shunning all sport'. Harald also recounted to the author the occasion when, having told Sir Ernest he was trying, unsuccessfully, to teach young Edward to fly, his father replied, 'Then teach him to sow some wild oats'!

In 1934, Sir Ernest had insisted that Edward should be co-opted to the Westland Board and rank equal with long-serving Stuart Keep, the general manager. Robert Bruce, then Westland's managing director, would not accept this ruling and resigned. When Geoffrey Hill, a renowned aerodynamicist and designer with Westland, learned that young Petter was to become technical director, he packed his bags as well.

During the next ten years Edward Petter demonstrated his innovative genius with designs for the Lysander, of which 1,652 were built, the Whirlwind, Welkin and Wyvern fighters, every one with unusual or unique features. 'Sometimes too many of them for their own good' recalled Harald Penrose. 'Like routing the Whirlwind's exhaust pipes through the fuel tank for example'. Then, in July 1944, when his long repeated demands to be appointed chief engineer with overall responsibility for design and production fell on deaf ears, he resigned from Westland and moved to English Electric Aircraft Division at Warton, Lancs to take the coveted chief engineer appointment. He took with him from Westland his designs and proposals for a twin-jet fighter-bomber which he developed to become the Canberra. It is interesting to compare Harald Penrose's description of Petter in 1931 with that given in 1944 when he left Westland. He was then described as 'intolerant of his colleagues, demanding for himself absolute control of the company in all its aspects' and being 'difficult, brilliant, eccentric, intense, and dictatorial'.

At English Electric, having seen his Canberra become the RAF's first jet bomber and take the world by storm, then successfully launching the big, complex Lightning Mach 2 plus fighter, Petter went all 'lightweight and simple'. It was in this frame of mind that he resigned from English Electric and, in October 1950, joined Folland Aircraft as deputy managing director. At that time, as noted earlier, Henry Folland was a sick man and on his retirement through ill-health in July 1951, Petter succeeded him as managing director. The new chief designer was Frederick Henry Pollicutt who joined Folland Aircraft from Bristol Aeroplane Co.

In August 1952 the Ministry of Supply (MoS) requested Folland Aircraft Ltd to undertake the design and development of a light ejector seat. The Specification called for a fully-automatic seat with a weight much less than 100lb and having an ejection velocity of 80ft per second. However, the initial Folland seat would have a 60ft per second ejection velocity. A lightweight ejector seat had been produced by the SAAB company in Sweden, some operating features of which had been criticised by the RAE and the Institute of Aviation Medicine (IAM) at Farnborough during its evaluation there. In May 1953 Folland Aircraft signed an agreement with SAAB which would supply technical details of its seat.

Preliminary design work at Hamble, carried out by Wing Commander D. Smith and Ivor Davies, quickly revealed that as the SAAB seat had no automatic feature and its firing system was unacceptable to the IAM, Folland decided to grasp the nettle and start from scratch with a seat design which would embody a basic SAAB feature. This was the use of twin ejection guns which formed part of the main seat frame structure and also acted as the guide tubes which, on ejection, moved in roller brackets secured to the seat bulkhead.

The then current trend of design in jet fighters was for more complex, bigger and therefore more expensive radar and missile-carrying all-weather aeroplanes such as the Gloster Javelin, English Electric Lightning and de Havilland Sea Vixen. As a result there arose a large body of opinion aimed at controlling this upward spiral. This led to the creation of the lightweight fighter concept in several countries. In Britain, Edward Petter was already contemplating the private venture design of such an aeroplane, the Folland Fo140 Gnat. He was firmly of the opinion that it could fill an important role in the struggle for air superiority, where numbers might be paramount, and in the destruction of bombers where extensive search equipment would not be necessary.

Meanwhile, Bristol Aeroplane Co.'s aero engine department at Filton was working on the design of a small turbojet engine for Folland's little fighter. This stemmed from a 3,000lb thrust engine intended for the Bristol 182 Red Rapier cruise-missile which was cancelled by the Government. Further private venture development created the 3,800lb thrust Saturn intended for the Gnat. Lack of Government support killed it off too. While Bristol persisted with the design of another small axial-flow engine, which would become the Orpheus, Petter produced designs for a prototype of his fighter, designated Fo139, powered with a 1,640lb thrust Armstrong Siddeley Viper engine.

Construction of this private venture prototype, named the Midge, began in 1953 at Hamble, from where it was to be taken by road to the Aeroplane and Armament Experimental Establishment (A&AEE) at Boscombe Down, Wilts. While this work proceeded a new Production Shop and Experimental Department building were completed, further factory floor areas were released for production purposes and additional design office staff were recruited.

After a 'dummy run' along the route from Hamble to Boscombe Down to check that, with wing tips removed, the Midge's resulting 19ft 4in wingspan could be threaded through a maze of roads, the complete aircraft was moved on an articulated vehicle to the A&AEE at 3 a.m. on 11 August 1954. A little over twelve hours later it was in the air. The pilot was Squadron Leader E.A. 'Ted' Tennant, the Company's chief test pilot, who had seen the aeroplane through from its mock-up stage to completion. He made a preliminary short 'hop' in the Midge, which had Folland's Class B markings G-39-1, before taking-off at precisely 4.39 p.m. after an unexpectedly long second 'hop'. Tennant then called the Control Tower 'Hello Boscombe. Midge airborne on first flight. I thought I should have to brake too hard if I had landed that time so I decided to complete the take-off'. Several hours later after some preliminary handling flights Tennant flew the Midge to Chilbolton, Hampshire, where Folland had already established a Flight Development Unit in an ex-RAF hangar.

This was a great day for all at Folland Aircraft – particularly for Edward Petter. Not only had he inspired yet another of his innovative aircraft designs and seen it fly successfully but, earlier in the year, following the retirement of H.F. Pollicutt, Folland's chief designer, Petter had become managing director and chief engineer. At last he was a 'company supremo' with responsibility for the direction of the Company's policy and for development of the Gnat, a new concept which he had pioneered.

During its flight development the Midge showed its transonic performance capabilities – in a dive, it must be said. The dives were started at about 37,000ft with Mach 1.0 being achieved at about 24,000ft and held for some six seconds during which a slight trim change was noticed. The handling characteristics were precise and good with the stall beginning at about 115mph and not fully developing until Tennant had the control column right back. The aircraft was stable in all three axes. All these data augured well for the Gnat.

With the necessary ten flying hours having been logged with the Midge it qualified to take part in the SBAC Display at Farnborough during 6-12 September 1954. In an overall Nordic blue colour scheme, the Midge's precise control in the roll with very crisp angular motion of the aeroplane were ably demonstrated by Ted Tennant who quickly captured the attention of spectators. The case for the light fighter was in everyone's mind that week.

About five weeks after the first flight Folland Aircraft made the Midge available to pilots of the A&AEE to fly it over a three day period. During that time five Establishment pilots flew it and fourteen flights were made. As this was not an official A&AEE evaluation the Establishment headed its report as 'A&AEE Preliminary "Appreciation".'

Because ground resonance tests had not been carried out, the A&AEE flight tests were limited to 450knots/520mph and 0.95 IMN and, because of the Viper engine, tests could not be made effectively above 30,000ft. Most aspects of flight were briefly looked at within these restrictions but spins and extreme side-slip were not investigated at all. Pilots were extremely impressed with the Midge. With certain exceptions they considered its flying characteristics to be highly satisfactory and its potential most promising. Its near-neutral stability and the light and effective elevator were well suited to the roles of ground attack or interceptor fighter. These characteristics were virtually the same over the tested ranges of Mach number, indicated air speed and height. No pitch-up was encountered despite energetic attempts to induce it.

The aileron control was relatively heavy and lacked self-centring due to high friction in the control system which necessitated more concentration than usual for instrument flying and also led to over-correction and Dutch-rolling on take-off. Some modification to the rudder system also was recommended, but only after spinning tests and cross-wind landings had been investigated.

The characteristics at the straight stall at 100knots/115mph were satisfactory, but a sharp yaw and wing drop to starboard occurred between 115-120knots/130-145mph and this led to a somewhat high approach speed of about 130knots/150mph. There was a fairly large nose-down trim change on lowering the landing gear and some slight buffeting. The airbrakes were powerful with some slight buffeting. The cockpit layout and pilot's view were good, although there were differing opinions from some pilots. The ground handling was criticised, but it was realised that the nosewheel castoring and brake installation were being improved.

The tests, though limited, showed that the Midge had very good aerodynamic properties. The most serious comments concerned the approach to landing condition where landing flaps were required, with the yaw and wing-drop occurring, well above the stall, needing to be suppressed.

The A&AAE 'Appreciation' summary recorded that, unless external stores introduced any new handling problems, the Gnat should be an excellent ground attack aircraft. With this limited testing, characteristics for the interceptor role also appeared to be good. Naval pilots shared the enthusiasm for the aircraft but emphasised the importance of improved approach characteristics if deck landings were to be considered.

This 'Appreciation' by such a skilled and critical authority was a massive boost for Petter and the Folland Company in general. The Midge returned to Chilbolton where the flight development programme was continued in the light of the A&AEE pilots' comments.

In the meantime the Bristol company had pulled out all the stops on the Orpheus and the first engine ran on 11 December 1954. By the end of May 1955 it had successfully completed a 150-hour Type Test. With this hurdle negotiated, work on the first Gnat, now under Petter's supreme control, moved up a gear or three and on 27 June 1955 the aeroplane was pushed out for initial engine running at Hamble.

On a lighter note, in the summer of 1955, Folland's Chilbolton site was invaded by a film production unit when the Midge appeared in a British film *Flame in the Skies*, co-starring with actor Kieron Moore. However, the aeroplane was in the safe hands of test pilot Squadron Leader Leslie 'Dick' Whittington who had joined the Company as assistant chief test pilot.

In layout the Gnat was almost identical to the Midge. The 22ft 2in span high-wing configuration with anhedral was unusual, as were the power-operated, inboard ailerons and lack of independently-operated flaps. This high-wing position, combined with the low-set tailplane, was reported to have been used to avoid excessive downwash from the wing striking the tailplane during turns and other manoeuvres and thus destroying its stabilising effect.

Because of its short span the wing was manufactured in one piece and could be changed if damaged in little more than eleven hours. In addition the wing was completely devoid of landing gear, fixed armament and tanks. These and other design features all helped to save weight. Inboard ailerons attached to the thicker part of the wing enabled an 8% thickness/chord ratio, light construction wing to be used. For landing the ailerons were drooped 20 degrees to minimise nose-up attitude. At high speed, inboard ailerons were more effective, producing about twice the rate-of-roll than outboard ailerons. Thus, for a given manoeuvre, they required less hydraulic power and a smaller jack. Doors attached to the fuselage-mounted nose and main landing gear units acted as air brakes when the gear was partially lowered. The monocoque fuselage carried side air intakes for the 3,285lb thrust Bristol BOr.1 Orpheus turbojet engine. The intakes also housed the two 30mm Aden guns, each of which had 150 rounds, sufficient for about six seconds firing. Folland's plastics department produced the one-piece cockpit canopy, which was hinged at the rear, and a lightweight, fully-automatic ejector seat was fitted. The production of windscreens and canopies was to become a rewarding facet of the Company's activities.

After its initial engine running which took place on the slipway at Hamble, the first Gnat prototype, G-39-2, was taken to Boscombe Down by road for its first flight. This took place on 18 July 1955 with Tennant flying it.

A Folland Aircraft advertisement in *Flight* magazine of 2 September 1955 announced 'The Gnat light fighter has all that is best in modern performance and equipment allied to unique manoeuvrability. Easy to make, maintain and operate, it springs from an intense concentration over the past four years of a new engineering team led by the man who designed the Canberra. In a world of increasing complications and many consequent setbacks we at Follands – together with the makers of the engine and many items of equipment – have recognised that there is room for a simple, efficient and versatile fighter of high performance. We are proud that the value of our idea is increasingly recognised among those who frame air policy in the countries of the free world'.

The Gnat programme got a real shot in the arm in March 1955 when it was announced in the House of Commons that the MoS was about to place an order for six pre-production Gnat F1s. The first of these, XK724, first got airborne on 26 May 1956. XK739 and XK740 were used for flight testing the Orpheus engine and the A&AEE received XK741 for performance and armament evaluation. When XK739 was written off at Chilbolton it was replaced by XN326 in 1959. Later XK767 was fitted with an hydraulically-powered 'all-moving' slab tailplane with twin screw-jacks for flight testing. This replaced the variable incidence tailplane which was electrically-operated. The fuel system had seven bag tanks in the fuselage holding a total of 174 gallons. The last of the six Ministry of Supply's Gnat F1s, bought back by Folland Aircraft, carried Class B marking G-39-3. In these Gnats cockpit pressurisation began at 15,000ft with a maximum differential of $3\frac{1}{2}$lb p.s.i. at 40,000ft and above. The ceiling was about 50,000ft and the maximum level speed was Mach 0.9. At a full load of around 6,500lb, the Gnat's 1957 published take-off performance was a 750 yards run to clear a 50ft screen under tropical sea-level conditions.

Then, on 26 September 1955, the Midge prototype was destroyed in an accident at Chilbolton. This aircraft had logged about 110 flying hours in the hands of more than twenty different pilots. Among them was Air Commodore P.C. Lal of the Indian Air Force (IAF) who was immediately impressed with the Midge's handling and performance. He saw its potential, which fired his enthusiasm for the light-fighter concept.

During 1954-1955 Hamble and Chilbolton had seen a vast number of tests associated with the Folland lightweight ejector seat. Some 450 tests of cordite charges to achieve exactly the right thrust to eject the seat and pilot without damage or injury; countless checks on weights and material strengths and a series of ejections of dummy 'pilots', all named Charlie, from a specially modified Gloster Meteor T7 two-seat, twin-jet trainer over Chilbolton.

All this culminated in the first 'live' ejection from the Meteor on a bitterly cold 21 December 1955 over Netheravon on Salisbury Plain. The principal 'players' were Major T.W. 'Dumbo' Willans, an ex-member of the Parachute Regiment's 1st Independent Pathfinder Platoon, who was currently a professional parachutist, and 'Dick' Whittington, Folland's pilot, who would be responsible for dropping Willans from the correct point in the sky at 5,000ft over Netheravon. Whittington described this historic event in dramatic style in the Folland company's house journal *Fanfare*. 'FIVE..FOUR..THREE..TWO..ONE..FIRE! There followed an almost imperceptible pause, then the familiar explosion occurred in the rear cockpit. I banked round steeply and saw the parachute open and a black speck – the seat – fall away through the clouds below. Dumbo Willans had just made the first live ejection in the Folland seat'. Some five weeks later, on a wet and windy 7 January 1956, Whittington again flew Willans in the Meteor for the second live ejection. A number of live ejections were made by Arthur Harrison of GQ Parachute Company Ltd, a Sergeant Sawyer and Sergeant Jimmy McLouchlin.

Although Gnat F1 fighters found no place in Royal Air Force squadrons, they created a great deal of interest in other countries. Finland, India and Yugoslavia were to turn this into firm orders. Following Air Commodore Lal's flights in the Midge in late 1954, Indian interest in the project was enhanced following a visit by Pandit Nehru, that country's Prime Minister, on a cold February day in 1955 to see Tennant fly the Midge. The following month Petter visited India and toured Hindustan Aircraft Limited's factory (HAL) at Bangalore where it was proposed that the Gnat could be licence-built. He also gave a presentation on the Gnat to senior Government officials and a large number of high-ranking Indian Air Force officers. Of vital importance were his talks with Air Marshal S. Mukerjee, chief of the Air Staff and his deputy Air Vice-Marshal A.M. Engineer. Then, in March 1956, Squadron Leader Suranjan Das came to England and flew the prototype Gnat at Chilbolton. Finally, on 15 September, Petter with L. Egan, Company secretary and Sir Reginald Verdon-Smith, Bristol Aeroplane Co. chairman and joint managing director, went to the private residence of Mrs V.L. Pandit, the Indian High Commissioner in London, where a contract was signed. It covered the supply of twenty-five Gnat F1 fighters built at Hamble plus spares and twenty complete pack-up kits of sub-assemblies and components for final assembly by HAL. Of the twenty-five Hamble-built Gnats, which were serialled IE1059 – 1083 in IAF service, twenty-three were produced specially for India; the other two were XK768/G-39-3 which became IE1059 with XN122 eventually becoming IE1064.

The first delivered IAF Gnat F1 flew on 11 January 1958 as G-39-5. It was transported by air in an IAF Fairchild Packet, serialled IK451, and was accepted as IE1061 on 30 January. Later deliveries of complete aircraft continued by sea until June 1960. Deliveries of pack-up kits began in 1959, the first being assembled by HAL at Bangalore and delivered to the IAF on 18 November. Assembly by HAL of Gnat kits from Folland Aircraft continued until late 1963.

While everyone was concentrating on exports to India, during the run-up to the September 1956 SBAC Display at Farnborough, a small three-view drawing was published in *Flight* magazine showing the possible layout of a new two-seat jet trainer. Probably overlooked by many of the magazine's readers, this was the version of the Gnat which was described as being intended as 'a single stepping-stone between *ab initio* instruction and operational flying'. Its main external features were a long cockpit canopy and conventional outboard ailerons.

There is an intriguing story about Edward Petter during one of his visits to India. At a meeting with very senior IAF officers and Government officials he was questioned about possible improvements to the IAF's Canberras which were being attacked by Pakistan Air Force F-86 jet fighters. Petter immediately sketched a modified Canberra, with swept wings and rear fuselage-mounted engines, which he thought could be built by Hindustan Aircraft Ltd!

Many of the first batch of Gnats to be delivered were allocated to the recently-formed Gnat Handling Flight at the Aircraft and Armament Testing Unit at Kanpur. The IAF produced all its own maintenance, operating and training procedures. The first HAL-assembled Gnat, using a Folland partially-completed airframe, was IE1072 which first flew late in 1959. No.23 'Cheetah' Squadron IAF was the first to re-equip with Gnats, all built by Folland, in March 1960 when it finally gave up its Vampire FB Mk 52s, a type which had been in IAF service for ten years. No.23 Squadron achieved operational status the following year with Nos 2 and 9 Squadrons becoming operational with the Gnat during 1962. The first all-HAL example, IE1205, first got airborne on 26 May 1962 with full production beginning the following year.

India was not alone in acquiring Gnat fighters; export orders were won in Yugoslavia and Finland, though for very modest quantities. Thirteen Gnat fighters were exported to Finland for the *Ilmavoimat* following an order, received on 17 October 1956, which put a fifty-one million Finnish marks price-tag on each aircraft. The main batch of twelve Gnats were serialled GN101 – GN112. The first one flew on 11 February 1958 and was delivered by air on 30 July 1958 for *Haviittajalaivue* 21 (21 Squadron) at Luonetjarvi in central Finland. During 1957 a decision in principle was made for licenced production of Gnats by Finland's Valmet Oy organisation, but this plan never got airborne.

To commemorate the forty-first Air Force Day on 6 March 1959, GN101's nose was inscribed with the name *Kreivi von Rosen* in memory of the man, Count von Rosen, who donated the first aircraft to the Finnish Air Force on that day in 1918.

Deliveries continued until October 1960 when the last aircraft left Chilbolton having been converted to carry a nose-mounted Vinten G95 camera system for the fighter-reconnaissance role. When an extra aircraft was added to the order, XN326, the last single-seat Gnat to have a British serial number and which had been flown by the A&AEE, was bought by Folland and similarly converted with cameras for Finland, becoming GN113. Gnats flew mainly with 11 Squadron, some having previously been flown by 21 Squadron. In total Finnish Gnats flew 6,083 hours. Gnat GN101 flew the last sortie on 24 October 1972 and is now exhibited in the Finnish Air Force Museum at Tikkakoski with a second one outside the Museum. Two other Gnats are preserved in Finland; GN103 as gate guardian at Halli air base and GN106 at the Finnish Aviation Museum at Helsinki's Vantaa Airport.

Yugoslavia ordered two for evaluation in 1958. During test flying which began on 7 June 1958, they carried Class B markings G-39-8 and G-39-9; these were removed before the first aircraft was taken by rail to Yugoslavia where it was accepted on 21 June 1958. The second Gnat was delivered in the same way arriving on 25 July 1958. In service with the *Jugoslovensko Ratno Vazduhoplovstvo* they were serialled 11601 and 11602. No further orders were received from this customer because the British and Yugoslavian Governments could not agree on the amount of offset for a future contract.

Petter's plans for the fully supersonic Fo143 Gnat Mk 2 were advancing by now and there were hopes that a prototype would fly in 1959. It was to have been powered with an up-rated Orpheus having simplified reheat, or 'wee-heat' as it became known, and a high-lift system to allow operation from short strips or aircraft carriers and a thinner 6% thickness/chord ratio wing. There were other design proposals but sadly none of these got much beyond the Project Design Office doors. But more of supersonics later. Of much more immediate importance was the work on the Fo144 Gnat T1 two-seat trainer, foreseen as a replacement for the Vampire T11 in RAF service. Such was the interest in this aircraft that an MoS order for a development batch of fourteen aircraft was being planned. These were to prove the viability of the project. An early element of the programme was aimed at assessing the Gnat T1's spin characteristics and recovery technique. Several one-fifth scale plastic-moulded models were produced by Armstrong Whitworth Aircraft at its Whitley Site for Folland Aircraft. Subsequently, these were dropped for spinning tests over the Larkhill Range on Salisbury Plain.

In August of that year Gnat F1, XN122, plus a spare Orpheus engine and ground support equipment, were taken by road to RAF Abingdon, Oxfordshire, loaded aboard a Blackburn Beverley heavy transport aircraft of No.47 Squadron and flown to Aden for tropical and armament trials. There it was flown in competition with a Jet Provost T3, XN117 and two Hunter F6s, XK150-151, as part of a programme to find a new RAF ground attack aircraft. On completion of the trials, on 8 September 1958 the Gnat and its equipment were reloaded and flown to the Aircraft and Armament Testing Unit at Kanpur in India. This aircraft was accepted as

IE1064. The Gnat was ruled out as a ground-attack aircraft, the Hunter ultimately being selected for this role.

While Folland Aircraft was occupied with Gnat fighter production for export, the Company was encountering mounting difficulties when confronted with the ever-increasing financial resources required to fund further aircraft development. In addition, the Government's rationalisation programme decreed that it would only place production orders with large conglomerate companies. Following discussions between Petter and Hawker Siddeley during the autumn of 1959, Folland Aircraft Ltd became a member of Hawker Siddeley Aviation Ltd. HSA undoubtedly recognised the Hamble company as a well-equipped, experienced and technically capable organisation. Petter, now a disillusioned man, retired to Switzerland where he died, aged 58, in 1968. His successors were Maurice J. Brennan, who became a director and chief engineer, and Joe Boulger became chief designer. While Petter was a difficult act to follow, forty-seven-year old Brennan, who had previously been chief designer with Saunders-Roe on the Isle of Wight, then assistant chief designer at Vickers-Armstrong (Aircraft) in Weybridge, Surrey, was a well-qualified aeronautical engineer and designer with great experience.

Folland 43/37 flying engine test bed aircraft dubbed 'The Frightful'. Here it is pictured in August 1941 with a 2,000hp Napier Sabre 24-cylinder, horizontally-opposed, liquid-cooled engine.

A neatly-cowled 1,700hp Bristol Hercules VIII 14-cylinder twin-row sleeve-valve air-cooled radial engine in a Folland 43/37 for flight testing in March 1942.

Serialled P1775 this Folland 43/37 is seen at Staverton, Gloucester in March 1942, with a Bristol Centaurus engine and four-blade propeller. What appear to be two carburettor air intakes and a lengthened exhaust pipe clutter the cowling.

Quantity production of fuselage nose sections for Bristol Beaufort torpedo/bombers. In the foreground are bomb beams for Vickers Armstrong Wellingtons and Warwicks.

A Warwick GR Mk II with Centaurus engines in November 1944.

A completed Seafire wing on a wheeled stand in the Folland Aircraft factory during the Second World War. The folding wing feature is clearly visible.

The Seafire wing assembly lines in the main hangar at Hamble.

This Spitfire MkVb was modified with floats and a redesigned tail unit. It stands outside the main hangar's giant up-and-over door awaiting flight trials. It first flew in this form in April 1945 and was shipped to Egypt in October where it flew from the Bitter Lakes.

Folland Pony electric truck assembly line at Hamble in September 1946.

'Crumbs'! A pair of Folland Pony electric trucks en route to a customer on 6 October 1947. These trucks were also known as Bush Dowty trucks.

Among the range of non-aviation products which helped to keep Folland's factory busy during 1946-1948 were domestic refrigerators. This model was described as the 'New type Power Master'.

A July 1948 view of the press shop and the large rubber press, seen here being loaded. It was capable of loading and forming a number of different components at the same time.

Folland Aircraft built the huge control surfaces for the 230ft span Bristol Brabazon and their ground handling equipment. This flap was delivered to Filton on 4 April 1947.

This giant transporter for the Brabazon's outer wing section is seen outside Folland's even bigger main assembly hangar door. Note the massive counter weight for the up-and-over door at the far end.

The Brabazon stands complete with its Folland-built flying control surfaces. This aircraft G-AGPW was first flown from Filton on 4 September 1949.

Dove wings seen being built at Hamble on 10 July 1948.

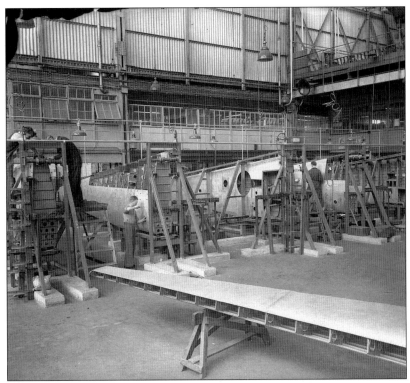

A de Havilland Dove with US stars and stripes on its fin. The clean lines of the wings are shown as the aircraft banks toward the camera.

Air-to-ground view of Folland's Hamble factory in 1950. The original British Marine Aircraft building rises high above later workshops and offices. Wartime roof camouflage is still visible. The slipway is bottom left.

Folland Aircraft's Board of Directors in September 1950. From left to right: R.J. Norton, T. Gilbertson (General Manager), W.E.W. Petter (Deputy Managing Director), H.P. Folland (Managing Director), C.L. Hill (Chairman), E.N. Egan (Secretary), E.C. Lysaght.

How the 'Chippy' got its wings. Assembly line showing various stages in the production of wings for the de Havilland Chipmunk two-seat basic trainer.

A row of Vampire wings stands alongside their assembly jigs in Summer 1950. Landing gear, wiring harnesses, pipes, flaps and ailerons are being fitted.

Hydraulic tests of a Vampire starboard main landing gear and flap hydraulic actuation systems prior to despatch from Hamble in 1950.

Concept model of a Gnat fighter in November 1951. Note the high 'T' tail unit and sharply swept wings. This was one of many configurations considered for the Gnat variants.

Having launched the Company's Apprenticeship scheme, Henry Folland, OBE, took a great interest in his apprentices' training. He is seen here with Mrs Folland on 20 November 1951 when the apprentices made a presentation on 'the Boss's' retirement. From left, front row: Edward Petter, Henry P. Folland, Mrs Folland and T. Gilbertson.

Folland Aircraft carried out development work for the proposed Red Dean air-to-air missile shown here carried by a Gloster Meteor F8.

Wing leading edge structures for the de Havilland Venom jet fighter leave a Folland Aircraft dispersal factory in Winchester Road, Southampton on 26 September 1952. The next-door neighbour, clearly, was into a different class of engineering.

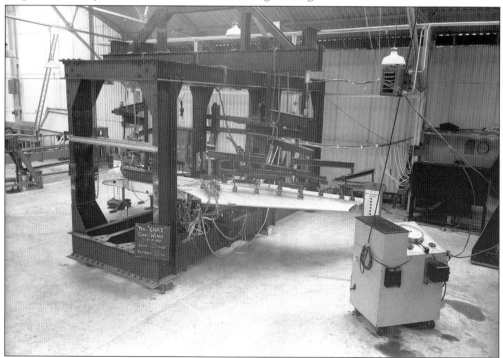

Front view of the Gnat wing in a structural test rig at Hamble in March 1953.

Photographed on 3 April 1953, the full-size mock-up of the Gnat fighter stands in the new experimental shop.

'Charlie', the dummy pilot, is test-fired on a Folland lightweight ejector seat during trials in May 1954. Here he has separated from the seat.

'Seven days to go'. The Midge is seen in the experimental shop on final trials of the hydraulic system on 23 July 1954, one week before roll-out.

A Folland-designed starter trolley for use with the Armstrong Siddeley Viper turbojet engine which powered the Midge.

This view looking forward under the Midge's starboard wing shows one of the tiny Dowty main landing gear units, its door and the fuselage bay into which it retracts.

The Midge's first time out of the hangar en route to the Sports Field area for initial engine running.

'All OK!' Folland engineers concentrate their attention under the Midge's fuselage during early engine runs with the Armstrong Siddeley Viper engine.

Seen on 3 August 1954, the completed Midge ready for moving by road to the A&AEE Boscombe Down for flight testing. This view shows the little aircraft's very clean lines.

On the 53-mile journey from Hamble to Boscombe Down airfield, a convoy of vehicles follow the Midge. People watch and take pictures while others carefully guide the important cargo through this village. Police assistance was sometimes required along the winding and often narrow roads to ensure the Midge's safe passage.

'Fifty-to-one on the Midge'. Fifty people either work on, look at or talk about the Midge being prepared for its first flight at Boscombe Down on the day it arrived there. One man works on the Fairey FD1 beyond them.

The new Midge, seen over the Hampshire countryside, with Class B registration G-39-1.

A publicity photograph which tells it all. At Chilbolton the Folland Midge is totally eclipsed by the huge Avro Lancaster B1, whose 33ft long bomb bay could have swallowed the little prototype with ease.

During September-October 1954 specialist engineers from the Royal Aircraft Establishment at Farnborough assisted with the ground resonance tests on the Midge in Hamble's experimental shop.

The new Folland Sports and Social Club House, much used today, opened on 31 May 1955.

Folland Aircraft employees enjoy the sunshine and some liquid refreshment on the terrace of the Club House.

The Bristol Orpheus engine and jet pipe installation in the Gnat fighter was a very snug fit, as seen in this May 1955 view.

The prototype Gnat, G-39-2, is rolled out of Hamble's experimental shop on 27 June 1955.

With the jet pipe 'blank' still firmly in place, the prototype Gnat is prepared for the first run of its Orpheus engine near the top of the slipway on roll-out day.

An expressive study in sound. Spectators and participants cover their ears as the Bristol Aero-Engine Division's technical representative opens wide the throttle during engine runs with the Gnat prototype.

'I don't think it was a mouse'. The Gnat's nose is raised high to drain excess fuel from the jet pipe after an unsuccessful 'wet start'.

The first Gnat was taken to the Folland Sports Field for photographing in May 1955.

The first Gnat airborne during its first flight on 18 July 1955.

A rare photograph of the Gnat and Midge together at Chilbolton on 20 July 1955. Identifying features are the Gnat's larger air intakes and tail-down attitude on the ground.

'I may look docile but just don't try anything'. Rintin the guard dog with his handler Harry Barker of Folland's Security force at Chilbolton on 12 June 1956. That's the Gnat prototype behind them.

Looking like the tails of a school of whales 'sounding', these Hawker Hunter tailplanes were being produced in Folland's Spring Road factory during August 1955.

A Hawker Hunter F6
photographed at Hawker
Aircraft's Dunsfold, Surrey,
aerodrome. Its tailplane was
made and delivered by
Folland Aircraft.

Bob Bennett easily holds the
lightweight fully-equipped
automatic Folland Mk1
ejector seat in July 1956.
Over 1,450 rig tests and 200
flight test ejections were
made during seat
development.

'Charlie' the dummy pilot is ejected from the Gloster Meteor during Folland ejector seat
trials in 1957.

Live ejections were made as a test from this Gloster Meteor T7 two-seat trainer. Four brave men tested Folland Mk 1 and Mk 4 seats. Pictured here is pilot Dick Wittington and Arthur Harrison in the rear cockpit.

Seat trials area at Hamble. Note the Meteor front fuselage in the background which was also used for seat firing trials. On the rig shown, the rear blast screen fitted to the Gnat T1 two-seat trainer is in place.

The first of the six Gnat F1 fighters ordered by the Ministry of Supply for evaluation is seen ready for transport to Chilbolton on 3 April 1956.

XK724 being pushed out for flight testing at Chilbolton on 23 May 1956. Note the inboard 'flaperons'.

A general view of Folland Aircraft's design office in October 1956. Slide rules and paper were still standard equipment for the design draughtsmen.

Gnat F1 XK740 over Southampton Water on 6 March 1957. While the Gnat obscures Netley and Hamble the Fawley refinery can be seen below it.

Scene on 3 April 1957 in Hamble's assembly hangar, where production of single-seat Gnat fighters was gathering pace. An Orpheus engine stands beside the aircraft on the extreme right.

A pair of Gnat F1s at the September 1958 SBAC Exhibition at Farnborough. The two white-overalled figures by XK741's wing tip are laying out the armament display; one of them holds a rocket projectile.

Gnat XK741 inside the huge T2A hangar at Chilbolton with fuel flow checks in progress. Tests were carried out with the aircraft at differing angles to simulate flows in climb attitudes.

The second MoS Gnat F1, XK739, first flew on 4 December 1956 at Chilbolton. It was written off in this crash landing on 15 July 1958 at that airfield. The airframe was used for tests until 1963 when it went to that happy hangar in the sky via Coley's scrap yard.

Four MoS Gnats inside Chilbolton's T2A hangar. The Folland ejector-seat trials Gloster Meteors are on the right.

In this view inside the T2A hangar two Gnat F1s with their rear fuselages removed can be seen.

This aircraft was initially serialled XK768 for the MoS but first flew as G-39-3 on 14 August 1957. It was then sold to India as IE1059 but crash-landed at Chilbolton on 18 March 1958 and was shipped to the customer as an instructional airframe.

Indian Gnats were delivered in an Indian Air Force Fairchild Packet as pictured here at Chilbolton. IE1063 is being loaded through the rear cargo doorway between the twin tail booms.

IE1069, the eleventh production aircraft for the IAF parked on a snow-covered apron at Chilbolton.

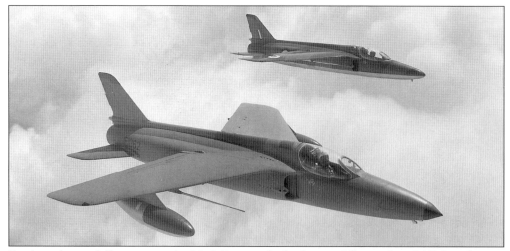

Brothers -but in different arms. An MoS Gnat in the background flies with an IAF Gnat having a radar-equipped nose and a brace of 66-gallon underwing drop tanks.

Each of these aircraft seen at Bristol Aero-Engines Ltd's Filton factory were powered by an Orpheus turbojet engine. From left: a Fiat G91 which won the NATO light fighter competition, Folland's little Gnat F1 and a North American Aviation F-86 Sabre.

Gnat F1 XN122 seen at Aden during August 1958 where it was undergoing tropical and gun-firing trials to find a new RAF ground attack aircraft. It was in competition with a Hawker Hunter and a Hunting Jet Provost. Note the sun shield over the open cockpit.

The daily 5 p.m. exodus at Hamble. Buses, cyclists, pedestrians, all busting to get home. Folland Aircraft employees leaving Cliffe Avenue Gate in September 1958.

Scene in July 1958 at Folland's Eastleigh dispersal factory where Gnat single-seat front fuselages are being assembled.

Gnat F1 production in the main assembly hangar with aircraft nearing completion.

An impressive line-up of Indian Air Force Gnat fighters being prepared for flight.

It's a cold outlook for this pair of Finnish Air Force Gnats seen on a snow-covered airfield. The wheeled ground-starting equipment was designed and manufactured at Hamble.

Engine-running with a Finnish Gnat. Note the tie-down restraining chains behind the main landing gear wheels.

Up in its own element above the clouds a Gnat, destined for Finland, is positioned for the cameraman.

No prizes for deciding to which Air Force this Gnat will be delivered. All the controls, switches and knobs are lettered in the Finnish language.

One of the two Gnat fighters purchased by Yugoslavia for evaluation. No further aircraft were bought but a significant number of Folland lightweight ejector seats were exported to that country.

Line-up of Gnats at Folland's Flight Development Unit at Chilbolton. It shows the progress made with production of this lightweight interceptor and ground attack aircraft for export to India and Finland and for the Ministry of Supply.

The first Gnat T1 trainer pictured on 25 May 1959 in Hamble's experimental hangar. In its roll-over assembly frame the landing gear and many system components have already been installed.

XM691, the first Gnat T1 variant, had conventional outboard ailerons.

Designer, pilot and aircraft. Edward Petter talks to chief test pilot Ted Tennant in the cockpit of the prototype Gnat trainer, XM961, on 1 September 1959 prior to its departure to the SBAC Display at Farnborough.

An MoS Gnat F1, XN326, keeps company with Tennant in the prototype Gnat T1 trainer as they head for the 1959 Farnborough Show.

The Folland Aircraft stand at the 1959 Farnborough Exhibition. It displayed models of the fighter and trainer Gnats plus a range of components for the aircraft. A vase of flowers was *de rigeur* on stands of that era.

Folland test pilots Dick Whittington, in the cockpit, and Mike Oliver (right) discuss training procedures for the new two-seater Gnat.

Three members of the Gnat family at Chilbolton. XM691 the first Gnat T1; the wing of XM696 has a saw-tooth leading edge, and XM693 is now the Gate Guardian at the Hamble factory.

Three

Folland's Hawker Siddeley Years

Although Hawker Siddeley was aware of work being done on variable-geometry, or 'swing-wing', techniques at Vickers-Armstrong by the great Barnes Wallis, father of the geodetic type structures and Second World War dam-busting bouncing bomb, it had not undertaken any detailed investigations itself. However, Stuart 'Cock' Davies, Hawker Siddeley's technical director, believed that Brennan's knowledge of variable-geometry, acquired during his time at Weybridge, should be applied to Folland's Gnat Mk 5 project.

At that time this little aeroplane, which was intended for interception and training roles, had a thin 6% thickness/chord wing of 24ft span and was seen as being powered by two Rolls-Royce RB153 engines which, it was estimated, would give it a Mach 2 plus top speed. The Company believed that it could fly by the end of 1962 and be in service within five years. Brennan adapted the design to have a variable-geometry wing to give it multi-purpose fighter/strike/trainer capabilities. Layouts Fo146, 147 and 148 were prepared. The RAF wasn't interested in any of these projects, which could have proved invaluable to Britain's variable-geometry research programme, and they were duly abandoned.

Attention was then focussed on air cushion vehicles. Maurice Brennan's involvement with ACVs stemmed from his time at Saunders-Roe when that company was designing and building the SR-N1 hovercraft during 1958-1959. This knowledge was brought to bear on Folland's GERM (Ground Effect Research Machine) programme which Folland was undertaking on behalf of Hawker Siddeley Group. Test rigs were built at Hamble and the GERM was produced two years later. However, further development work and involvement with air cushion vehicles was terminated in 1963.

Because the Gnat trainer's fuselage differed only in detail from the fighter, many components were common to both variants. The pupil and instructor had tandem Folland ejector seats, the production aircraft having 80ft per second ejection velocity seats which made runway-ejection a possibility. Fuel tanks were moved within the fuselage and the wing was modified to become 'wet'. The guns were deleted and other equipment was re-positioned in the nose. A one piece, clear-view canopy, hinged at the rear, covered both crew members in a pressurised cabin. The wrap-around windscreen was also made from one piece of acrylic.

To meet the take-off and landing distances and speeds specified for the trainer, a larger but thinner 7% thickness/chord ratio wing with 30 per cent more area than the fighter, conventional outboard ailerons and split flaps were used. The tailplane and fin areas were also increased. Except for the rudder, the trainer's flying controls were fully-powered, but with manual-reversion in the event of power failure. A standby hydraulic accumulator in each control system provided sufficient power for recovery should the failure occur while the aircraft was executing an unusual or difficult manoeuvre. Provision was made for four under-wing pylons to carry a range of stores which included fuel tanks, rocket pods, bombs and possibly missiles.

The Gnat T1 was powered by a 4,230lb thrust Bristol Siddeley Orpheus Mk 100 turbojet. The aircraft's performance was similar to that of the fighter with a maximum Mach 0.9 at sea level and Mach 0.97 at the tropopause. A shallow dive produced supersonic speeds of about Mach 1.15. The trainer's climb rate was good, the aircraft reaching 40,000ft within seven minutes, and its ceiling was above 50,000ft. A typical training sortie of one hour's duration was attainable, which could be extended to two hours when slipper tanks were used. A major feature of the Gnat was its structural fatigue life of 5,000 hours. The first Ministry of Supply order came in March 1958 and the first pre-production Gnat T1, XM691, was flown on 31 August 1959. This left just a week for the aircraft to log ten hours flying before it could be flown in Farnborough's SBAC Display. Both it and the Gnat F1, XN326, were flown during the week. Subsequently, XM691 was used for flight evaluation by the Company and at the A&AEE.

The first six Gnat T1s were flown with short nose cones. As manufacture proceeded with the first fourteen pre-production Gnat T1s, XM691-698 and XM704-709, they were extensively test flown and evaluated by the Central Flying School at RAF Little Rissington. The first four aircraft were used initially by Hawker Siddeley Aircraft for various trials during 1959-1966; the fifth one went to Bristol Siddeley Engines at Filton for Orpheus development flying on 18 July 1960 and was joined there by the fourth Gnat on 25 November 1966. By the time the last one, XM709, had flown in January 1962, the type had been ordered into production some two years earlier with a contract for thirty aircraft. The first production Gnat T1, XP500, first flew on 25 June 1962 and was delivered to the A&AEE the following month. It went back to Dunsfold then to Hamble for modification work before being issued to No.4 Flying Training School (FTS) at Valley, Holyhead on 28 February 1964. Some thirteen years later it was being 'cannibalised' for spares both at Valley and No.19 Maintenance Unit at St Athan, Glamorgan.

The first order for Gnat T1s was followed by further orders for twenty in July 1961 and forty-one in March 1962. Aircraft in these three orders were serialled XP500-516 and XP530-542; XR534-545 and XR567-574 with the last one being XR948-955, XR976-987, XR991-999 and XS100-111.The last Gnat T1 first flew on 9 April 1965 and was delivered to the Central Flying School (CFS) at RAF Little Rissington, Gloucestershire, high in the North Cotswolds, and became a Red Arrows aircraft.

In the meantime, with the lease on Chilbolton airfield rapidly running out, Hawker Siddeley decided to rationalise its test flying facilities, dispose of the Chilbolton site and move all flight testing of Gnats to its Dunsfold, Surrey, airfield. The first Hawker Siddeley Gnats, as they were now known, to arrive at Dunsfold from Chilbolton on 20 February 1961 were three T1s, XM691-2 and XM696 plus XK741, the sole remaining Gnat F1 fighter. Later the two Meteor T7s, WA690 and WF877, which had been modified for testing the Folland ejector seats, flew into Dunsfold. Four days later five more Gnats arrived. It was quite a circus.

Gnat production continued at Hamble with production aircraft being taken to Dunsfold for final assembly, and XP500 made its first flight from there. The second one, XP501, was the first to enter RAF service when it went to the CFS on 5 November 1962; two days later XP502 joined No.4 FTS at Valley where the first advanced flying course for pilots who had had initial training on the Jet Provost, began in 1963. A cockpit procedure trainer was introduced at an early stage and marked the first use of such a 'simulator' by Flying Training Command. Pupil pilots there received about seventy hours on the Gnat, which included thirty hours solo, before going to one of the Operational Conversion Units where they flew the type which equipped the squadron to which they would be posted.

While the Gnat F1 fighter had never entered RAF service the two-seat Gnat T1 was envisaged for a much more militant role than that of training. In December 1962 the US Secretary for Defence, Robert McNamara, and President John F. Kennedy decided to cancel the Douglas Skybolt air-launched ballistic missile programme for political, financial and technical reasons. Britain was basing its independent deterrent force on Skybolts carried either by RAF Bomber Command's Avro Vulcans or possibly by specially-equipped Vickers VC10 aircraft. With Skybolt's cancellation the rug was pulled from under this British plan.

During 1963 a number of alternative schemes were sought and one of these, dreamed up by the A.V. Roe company, was to carry three piloted Gnats under a Vulcan Mk 2. One was to be partially recessed into the Vulcan's bomb bay, with the others carried by the under-wing attachments intended for Skybolt. The Gnats, which would have been launched at a predetermined point, would have been armed with strike weapons. Although the Gnat T1s would have carried extra fuel tanks, the chances that they would have been able to return to their base seemed unlikely. However, as late as 1971-1972, as an exercise Gnat T1 trainers flew in close formation with Vulcans simulating Soviet bombers carrying stand-off weapons to attack UK targets.

It was in 1964 that the Gnat T1 first became more widely known to the British public. In that year No.4 FTS formed its own aerobatic team and, during June and July, eight aircraft, XR986-987 and XR991-996 were delivered to Valley for the team. With their Gnats painted bright yellow the team was named the Yellowjacks and flew a small number of displays that season. In October these aircraft went to RAF Kemble, Gloucestershire, for use by another team which succeeded the 'Jacks'. This was the newly-formed Royal Air Force Formation Aerobatic Team – the renowned Red Arrows. In February 1965 the 'Reds' moved to nearby RAF Fairford to join the CFS Gnats. In September 1966 they moved back to Kemble after a busy display season during which the Team was invited to Jordan by King Hussein, a staunch supporter of British aviation. When the CFS Gnats left Kemble in April 1976 the Team became designated the 'CFS Detachment'. The 'Reds' flew Gnats until 1980, by which time they had given 1,305 public displays world-wide. Their unrivalled mastery of the art of providing spectators with a continuous flowing spectacle earned them world-wide acclaim. As their pilots pointed out, the highly manoeuvrable Gnat Trainer was a delight to handle, even in turbulent conditions close to the ground. Its controls were crisp and sensitive and the rate of roll of their particular aircraft was very rapid. The subscription *Eclat* on the Red Arrows badge – this word meaning 'sparkling' or 'brilliant' – was the most apt and succinct description of the 'Reds' display.

With the introduction of the Gnat T1 there were some changes in the RAF's flying training. Folland Aircraft Ltd itself was also experiencing changes. It was not alone. The 1960s were a time of change for the entire British aircraft industry which, under Government pressure, was being rationalised and reshaped with two major aircraft groups of companies – Hawker Siddeley and British Aircraft Corporation – and two engine groups – Bristol Siddeley and Rolls-Royce – finally emerging. As a member company of Hawker Siddeley Group, Folland Aircraft was to be subject to numerous changes during the ensuing years. It also became involved with production of components for aircraft being manufactured by other Group companies. During the 1960s and early 1970s when production of some 370 twin-turboprop HS748 short haul air transports was in full swing at A.V. Roe's Manchester factories, Folland Aircraft built a substantial quantity of wings for early batches of these aeroplanes.

In July 1963 Hawker Siddeley Group reorganised its aircraft manufacturing business into Divisions; thus Folland became part of the Hawker-Blackburn Division of Hawker Siddeley Aviation Ltd, a new company which, with Hawker Siddeley Dynamics Ltd, had been formed by Hawker Siddeley Group on 1 January 1963. Folland was about to make a major contribution to the development of the Hawker P1127 and Kestrel, the forerunners of the Harrier.

As the manufacture of the Kestrel prototypes at Hawker Siddeley's Kingston-upon-Thames factory neared its completion, interest was being shown in the possibility of a two-seat trainer. In July 1964 it was decided that a feasibility study should be undertaken by the Hamble design office. On 30 July R.K. Page, the chief project engineer at Hamble, made the first of a series of visits to Kingston to discuss the probable changes to the existing design. At that time the RAF had no practical experience of operating V/STOL aeroplanes, this being confined to the P1127 prototypes; thus, the Air Staff were not equipped to produce a definitive V/STOL trainer requirement. By the end of 1964 the Hamble feasibility study of a P1127 two-seater was completed and given to the Ministry of Aviation. This was only the beginning of the Hamble company's part in the creation of the two-seat Harrier T2 and T4.

Before this, however, Hamble craftsmen were to become involved with one of Britain's more esoteric and politically sensitive military aircraft programmes. In around 1964 the Company received instructions to build a mock-up of the port wing of a new supersonic VTOL strike fighter being designed by the Hawker Siddeley design team at Kingston-upon-Thames. Its leader was Ralph Hooper. The aircraft was designated the P1154 and was to have been the production version of the P1127/Kestrel VTOL 'technology demonstrators'. It had a 26ft span shoulder wing with a 42.2 degree leading edge sweep and thickness/chord ratios of 6.2% at the root and 5.1% at the tip where a bullet fairing housed the retracted outrigged balancer landing gear units. It was a complex metal mock-up of the wing complete with systems, installations and flying control equipment. Mock-ups of the fin and rear fuselage also were completed.

By 4 February 1965 Hamble had produced wind tunnel models and had designed, built and installed six assembly jigs for P1154 wings with production already begun. Similarly, front fuselage assembly jigs stood ready for use. But two days earlier Prime Minister Harold Wilson had announced in the House of Commons that his Labour Government had cancelled the P1154. Few people, even within the two companies, knew that metal had been cut for this very advanced aeroplane. Two other advanced aircraft projects were also cancelled; the well known TSR2 which had already flown, and the Hawker Siddeley HS681 VTOL heavy transport aircraft. However, Folland went on to build large numbers of front and rear fuselage sections and empennages for Harrier variants. As the de Havilland/Hawker Siddeley Trident three-jet airliner was being introduced its wings and tailplanes were being built in Hamble's main assembly hall and delivered to Hatfield for final assembly to the aircraft.

In India the Indian Air Force Gnats played a major role during the war with Pakistan, which began on 1 September 1965, with many combat patrols being flown over various battle areas. Although several were shot down the IAF was well pleased with Folland's little fighter and four more squadrons were equipped with it. The Gnat was again called into defensive operations during the first hours of Pakistan's air strikes against Indian positions on 22 November 1971, in a second conflict which lasted well into December.

The design of the Gnat F1 fighter was transferred to Hindustan Aircraft Limited in India on 19 July 1974 through a joint agreement which also assigned marketing rights to that company. This, in turn, led to further development of the aircraft which materialised as the HAL Ajeet – meaning 'Invincible' – which had several modifications to the Gnat fighter's basic design. These included an up-rated Orpheus engine and a 'wet' wing with integral fuel tanks. This enabled the under-wing pylons to be used to increase the fire-power by carrying rocket pods or bombs in addition to the fixed 30mm cannon armament. The Folland ejector seat was replaced by a Martin-Baker seat, a much improved Ferranti weapons sight was installed plus updated avionics and navigation equipment. A two-seat trainer Ajeet was also produced. It retained the combat capability of the single-seat Ajeet but had a 4ft 6in longer fuselage to accommodate the extra seat. The prototype, E2426, made its initial flight on 20 September 1982. Later it recorded a sea level top speed of 665mph and a service ceiling of 46,000ft. Unfortunately it was lost in an accident during the following December. The second prototype, E2427, first flew on 7 September 1983, by which time the IAF had a stated requirement for eighteen Trainers with twelve being needed for the Indian Navy. In total 235 Indian Gnats were built, plus ninety single-seat Ajeets. The proposed programme to produce a two-seat Ajeet trainer was abandoned shortly after the first of the two aircraft built was lost in an accident.

Throughout the 1960s, the Hamble factory was kept busy with a range of components and sub-assemblies for a number of Hawker Siddeley aeroplanes. Among these, perhaps the Harrier was the most important at that time, with the Hamble factory being the sole source of the front and rear fuselages for the Harrier GR.1 and later, the re-designed rear fuselages for the two-seat Harrier T2 and its longer front cockpit and canopy. A good deal of design and development work had been done on this canopy by the Company's plastics department, with new moulding techniques being evolved. Other Harrier components included the fin and rudder, tailplane, airbrake and gun pods.

During the 1970s the success of these specialised techniques led to new work on canopies for the Hawker Siddeley HS1182 (later the Hawk) two-seat, advanced jet trainer and multi-role variants. Working with Hawker Siddeley's Kingston-on-Thames design team, development was centred on special high vision canopies with large transparencies and miniature detonating cord escape systems and stretched acrylic windscreens.

In 1971 the production of a range of components and sub-assemblies for the Airbus A300 and A310 began at Hamble. It included leading edge assemblies, machined leading edge ribs, track and jack cans and titanium engine pylons. This was the start of a long-running programme which has continued ever since. During this programme's development Hamble was tasked with building the leading edge bird-strike test structure.

While this work was in progress the Hamble factory was busy with production of Hawk rear fuselages, nose cones, windscreen, cockpit canopy and various items of equipment for multi-role variants. Another major programme has been the production of spares in support of the RAF and export Hawks, the latter variants having been bought by more than a dozen countries. Later, similar components were to be produced for the British Aerospace/McDonnell Douglas T-45 Goshawk, which was closely evolved from the Hawk for the US Navy's T45 Training System. Hamble again worked closely with McDonnell Douglas in the development of the escape system and in the support of the ejection trials conducted at China Lake, in the USA.

The Folland GERM (Ground Effect Research Machine) and a very distinguished audience. From left to right: -?-, Air Marshal Sir Richard 'Batchy' Atcherley (Executive Director – Gnat Sales, Hawker Siddeley Aviation), -?-, Maurice Brennan (Folland Chief Designer), Sir Thomas Sopwith (President, Hawker Siddeley Group) and Digby Brade (Folland Managing Director).

Taking two years to design and build, the Folland GERM is seen on the beach with Southampton Water behind it on 30 March 1961.

The ubiquitous Coventry Climax engine, which began life as the power unit for a small Civil Defence trailer fire pump in the Second World War, provided the power to drive the GERM's lift and ducted propulsion fans.

Although the dummy pilot looks a bit wide-eyed with apprehension, he occupies a Folland Mk 4 lightweight fully-automatic ejection seat. It was standard fit in the RAF's Gnat T1 advanced trainer.

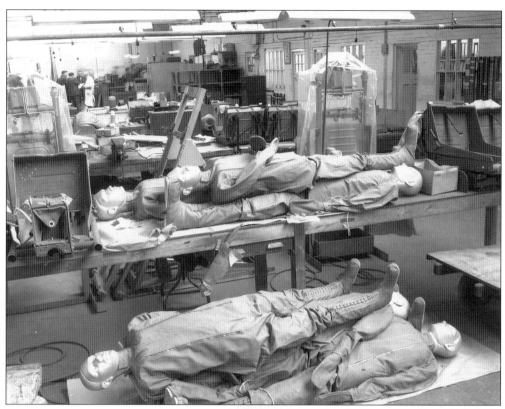

A view of the 'seat shop'. Among the ejection seats anthropomorphic dummies are prepared for their next mission!

This is for real! Dressed for the high altitude ejection test, Sergeant Sawyer sits strapped into the Folland Mk 4 seat.

Gnat T1s on the production line in August 1961. Steps and trestles were all of minimum height as much of the Gnat's airframe was accessible from ground level.

Fitting out the engine bay of a Gnat T1.

70

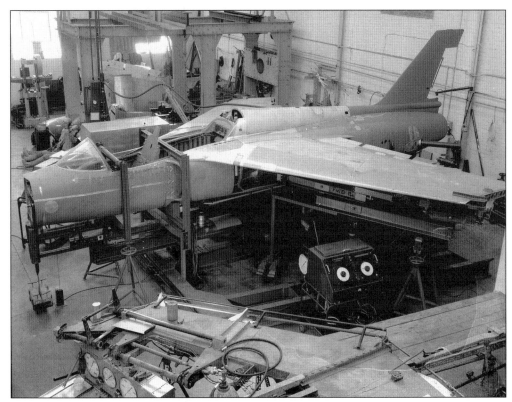

A test specimen Gnat T1 in the strength rig at Hamble. In the foreground is a flying control hydraulic system test rig.

The first two-seat Gnat, XM691, overflies Southampton Water with the Folland factory in the background.

A Gnat trainer model in the wind tunnel exploring future design changes.

The multi-spar skeleton framework of a Gnat trainer's wing in a main build jig.

Gnat cockpit procedure trainer built for No.4 Flying Training School at RAF Valley to modernize training methods and techniques.

The third pre-production short-nose Gnat T1 en route to the SBAC Display on 5 September 1960.

Folland produced a large number of wings for the Avro/HS 748. These wings being built in Hamble's main assembly hall were photographed on 7 July 1961.

This HS748 twin-turboprop airliner flies on its Hamble-constructed wings.

The Gnat trainer production line in February 1962. The aircraft in the foreground is on jacks to enable landing gear functioning to be checked.

XM709, the last of the fourteen pre-production Gnat T1s. The Folland Mk 4 ejection seats are clearly visible in this view of the aircraft parked on the apron at Dunsfold.

This photograph, taken in February 1962, shortly after the arrival of the first Gnat trainer at the Central Flying School, RAF Little Rissington, Gloucestershire, shows from left: the CFS Commandant, Air Commodore H.P. Connolly, DFC, AFC, AFM; Air Marshal Sir Richard Atcherley, KBE, CB, AFC and the Air Officer Commanding-in-Chief, RAF Flying Training Command, Air Marshal Sir A. 'Gus' Walker, KCB, CBE, DSO, DFC, AFC, MA.

Gnat T1, XP537, was delivered to the Central Flying School on 17 May 1963. It is seen at RAF Little Rissington with a Vampire T11 trainer which it replaced.

Folland Aircraft, now a member of Hawker Siddeley Aviation, positioned a yellow Gnat T1, XM698, in the 1962 Farnborough Show's Static Park. Next to it is the Hawker P1127, XP972, and the scarlet and white Hawker Hunter T66A, G-APUX. Across the roadway on the left is Handley Page's Herald 200, CF-MCK, with XP841, the HP115 delta -winged low speed research aircraft on its left and BOAC's VC10, G-ARTA, further right.

A Gnat trainer's 'front office'. The large left instrument is the attitude indicator, with the navigation display unit on the right. At the top from left are the airspeed indicator, altimeter and Mach meter. TACAN and ILS volume controllers are on the right side console.

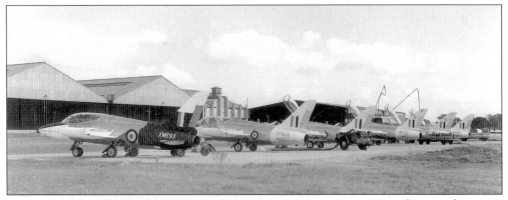

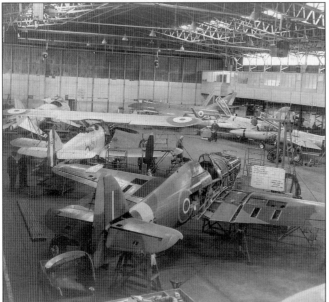

A morning line-up of production and flight development Gnats at Dunsfold on 27 September 1963. Part of the nearest aircraft's rear fuselage has been tufted. Tufts were also applied to the starboard wing's upper surface for spinning trials. Various strakes were fitted on the nose and rear fuselage for evaluation.

Gnats among the Hawker thoroughbreds. Seen in Dunsfold's flight shed in 1965. The shapes and sizes of the Hart, Hurricane, Hunter and P1127 contrast sharply with those of the diminutive Gnat trainers.

A section of CFS Gnat T1s. The nearest Gnat, XM706, was one of the pre-production batch but was modified to full production standard. XM709, the last pre-production aircraft, was delivered to the CFS in February 1962 where it remained in service for nine years.

The 1964 Yellowjacks formation aerobatic team wait in their cockpits for their display time to arrive. The one-piece acrylic canopy is well shown in this photograph.

A Red Arrows Gnat T1 pictured in the team's 1967 paint scheme. The doors on the landing gear, which is partially lowered, doubled as air brakes.

'Now, that's low!' A Red Arrows pilot flew his Gnat down to head height for this dramatic photograph. The shadow on the ground indicates how low it was.

Four Gnat T1s of No.4 Flying Training School based at RAF Valley, Anglesey, formate over the North Wales coastline.

A No.4 FTS aircraft taxies out to the runway, resplendent in its new and final red and white livery. The Gnat served with this squadron for sixteen years. No.4 FTS flew its last twelve-aircraft formation on 7 November 1978.

A display and conference model of the Hawker P1154 produced in December 1964. This was the RAF version; a Royal Navy variant was also planned.

Known only to a small number of Hawker Aircraft people, Folland built full-scale mock-ups of several major components for the P1154 supersonic VTOL fighter. This hitherto unpublished photograph dated 26 November 1964 shows the port wing.

By 4 February 1965 quantity production of P1154 wings had already begun in these six jigs at Hamble. In this photograph P1154 fuselage jigs can be seen further along in the same row.

Folland ejection seats await final inspection in the packing and despatch department during January 1965. Four Mk.1 seats are for Yugoslavia and two Mk.4s are for RAF Gnat T1s. In total some 800 seats were built.

'All work and no play makes Jack a dull boy' was a good Victorian philosophy. This float in the July 1965 Hamble-le-Rice Carnival procession shows that there was still a lot of fun to be had 100 years later.

One of Folland's long-running contracts was the ten-year production of tailplanes for de Havilland's Trident three-jet airliner. This photograph shows part of the structure prior to skinning.

This May 1965 scene at Hamble included wings for the de Havilland Trident, trailing edge uppermost, in their assembly jigs.

A Trident, G-ARPC, of British European Airways, lands at Farnborough during the SBAC Display on Sunday 9 September 1962. Parked in the background are No.74 Squadron's English Electric Lightning fighters, designed by Edward Petter before he joined Folland Aircraft.

This 'slipper' fuel tank for the Blackburn Buccaneer low-level strike aircraft is seen readied for inspection in March 1965.

A Blackburn Buccaneer is catapult-launched from the deck of the aircraft carrier HMS *Eagle*. The underwing 'slipper' tanks are clearly visible.

This January 1965 Hamble mock-up for a Harrier two-seat trainer aircraft incorporated Folland Mk.4 lightweight ejection seats. The re-styled cockpit and canopy configuration make an interesting comparison with the definitive design in the two-seat Harrier.

Assembly of Harrier T2 rear fuselages inverted in their jigs. Behind is a single-seat Harrier rear fuselage, B189. The man on the left staging works on a Hawk rear fuselage while the centre rear jigs carry Trident wings.

The fifth completed Harrier T2 rear fuselage immediately after being removed from its assembly jig.

Harrier fin production line at Hamble in 1975. Skin pins hold the outer skin in position prior to riveting.

The second Harrier GR1 to be built, XV277, was mainly used for development flying at Dunsfold and for stores clearance trials at A&AEE Boscombe Down. Hamble built GR1 front and rear fuselages, canopies, empennages and items of role equipment.

Harrier T2, XW175, seen in the hover mode, was the second two-seat aircraft. Initially used for development flying, it is currently flown at Boscombe Down in support of the Joint Strike Fighter programme and is designated the VAAC aircraft (Vectored-thrust Aircraft Advanced Flight Control).

Early manual moulding of Hawk canopy shells. When a bell rang everyone involved grasped a side and pulled it down over the heated mould block which flowed with grease. Hot work! Today this process is automated.

Folland ejection seats originally proposed for use in the HS1182 two-seat jet trainer project were used in this mock-up and driven along Dunsfold's runway to check the forward vision during landing. The HS1182 became the Hawk but, for commonality with the Jaguar and Tornado, Martin Baker Mk10B ejection seats equipped this new trainer.

The pre-production Hawk, XX154, was first flown by Duncan Simpson, Hawker Aircraft's chief test pilot, during the evening of 21 August 1974. The rear fuselage, canopy and windscreen for all Hawks originated at Hamble.

A trio of Hawks from RAF Valley fly above clouds. XX164 was from the Central Flying School, XX166 and XX170 belonged to No.4 Flying Training School.

Four

Now we're British Aerospace at Hamble

On 17 March 1977 the Royal Assent was given to a Bill which had long been debated in Parliament. This was the Aircraft and Shipbuilding Industries Act 1977 which, among other things, proposed that the issued share capital of Hawker Siddeley Aviation, Hawker Siddeley Dynamics, (Holdings), British Aircraft Corporation and Scottish Aviation should be vested in a new nationalised corporation named British Aerospace plc. This company came into being on 20 April 1977 with the Hamble organisation becoming part of the Kingston-Brough Division. On 1 January 1978 the old names of the constituent companies disappeared, much to the chagrin of many thousands of people in those companies and very many more outside them.

Despite these name changes production and development work continued on Harrier and Hawk aircraft with production for the Sea Harrier FRS1 variant also in hand. Of note was the addition of the British Aerospace/McDonnell Douglas AV-8B to the Harrier family with full-scale development being contracted and the initial batch of rear fuselages being tooled and built at Hamble.

On 17 June 1980, very soon after his appointment as Chairman of British Aerospace, Sir Austin Pearce visited the Hamble site and toured the factory and offices. He was impressed with the range of components, sub-assemblies and equipment being produced and particularly with the transparencies, composites and elastomers sections of the factory. This visit so early in Sir Austin's new role underlined the importance attached to the Hamble company by the British Aerospace Board. By this time Dennis Corbett had become divisional director and general manager with Ambrose Barber as executive director and deputy general manager with responsibility for Hamble. Ambrose Barber succeeded Corbett on his retirement.

New Year's Day 1981 saw the flotation on the Stock Exchange of British Aerospace plc. Sir Austin Pearce returned to Hamble on 5 October 1982 to open the new computer-numerically-controlled machine shop and to view the other newly-built facilities to accommodate the increasing pace of the Airbus programme and other work. In early 1984 Hamble was moved again within the BAe organisation, this time to the Weybridge Division. However, this was to be short-lived: two years later the Company became part of British Aerospace's Military Aircraft Division. There it remained until January 1989 when it was restructured as a wholly-owned subsidiary of British Aerospace. Renamed Aerostructures Hamble Ltd (AHL), it became part of British Aerospace Enterprises which was establishing 'centres of excellence'. AHL was charged with developing aerospace and defence markets for aerostructures and role equipment in the UK and internationally, but with attention being paid to achieving excellence in its specialised markets for non-metallic products. For some forty years similar product ranges and production techniques had been part of the Hamble company's armoury in the fight for sub-contract business.

But did these name changes really change the basic character of this well-established Hamble company? Managing Director John Perry didn't think so. 'The formation of a separate Company has placed on us all this great opportunity to be part of something outstandingly good – and at the same time earn a livelihood.' he wrote in the first issue of Aerostructures Monthly Review in January 1989. 'What we are going to be outstandingly good at is providing the Aerospace and Defence Industry with a design and manufacturing service at the right price, on time and of adequate quality, because that is what the competitive market demands'. This was the challenge which Aerostructures Hamble faced and which the Company was to meet in full. With hindsight, which is usually 100 per cent, BAe had neatly packaged the Hamble company not only as a profit centre but also for sell-off, if necessary, at a later suitable moment. This was further facilitated later in the year when AHL took over from BAe ownership of the land and buildings at the Hamble site. Previously AHL had been a tenant of BAe, paying rent and needing permission before undertaking alterations or additions.

As will have been recognised in earlier chapters, a special skill exploited by the Company since the 1950s was the design and production of cockpit canopies and windscreens, first for the Gnat and then for a range of aircraft. The Company pioneered the draped acrylic and the 'blown' pressure-moulded one-piece canopy for tandem crew configuration. Both these techniques have been used worldwide in fighter and trainer aircraft transparency production. Since then Aerostructures Hamble has maintained its specialisation in transparencies for these applications. In addition cabin windows, blast screens, quarter and navigation lights and similar items are produced. With the advent of stretched acrylic, AHL developed creep forming techniques for the Hawk trainer windscreen in the early 1970s. This made possible a lightweight unit with good impact resistance which also possessed the Grade 1 optical qualities necessary for weapon sighting Head Up Display symbology. The manufacture and development of the canopy and windscreen for the EAP technology demonstrator aircraft were undertaken as a learning-curve exercise for creating Eurofighter transparencies.

In compliance with BAe Enterprises' policy of achievement of excellence in non-metallic materials, AHL expanded its work on Glass Reinforced Plastics. This material had been used for Gnat components and for Blackburn Buccaneer nose radomes. Later production was extended to include Sky Shadow missile domes, pylon, fin fairings and tips, aerial covers, cabin interior panels and air conditioning ducts for Nimrod, VC.10, Trident, Hawk, Harrier and Airbus aircraft.

The emergence of new fibre materials and resins prompted new thinking by Aerostructures Hamble in the creation of aircraft structural components. Using autoclave or vacuum bag techniques, large secondary structural elements in glass or polyamide fibres (Kevlar) or composite hybrids both as monolithic or honeycomb sandwich assemblies are now produced. AHL's plastics facilities were regularly updated and expanded alongside design studies of newly emerging materials using computer-aided stress analyses to assist in understanding the complex behaviour of these composites. With the capability to design, develop, tool and manufacture products in all these non-metallic materials, AHL has a unique combination of state-of-the-art technologies with a skilled and experienced work force which has earned a reputation for product excellence.

During September 1989, when British Aerospace Commercial Aircraft Division at Filton delivered the six hundredth pair of Airbus wings, AHL's design office was working on Airbus A330 and A340 trailing edge ribs and panels; in addition it was carrying out a weight-saving exercise on an outboard wing section. Other work in hand included A300B and A310 wing sub-assemblies and components, Saab 340 wing root panels, production of Hawk fuselage assemblies, BAe 146 spines and fairings, with new orders for Sea Harrier FRSII components, Harrier GR5 gun pods, ATP engine nacelles plus spares and repairs for a number of aircraft including the Tornado, Fokker F28, Hunter and Phantom. These orders included aircraft ground equipment.

An unusual, if not unique, task undertaken by the Company was the machining of a 24ft square acrylic sheet depicting some of the historical events which have taken place at Brooklands. Hamble created the initial design and the NC programmes used in the machining process which required some fifty hours to complete. The finished sheet was mounted on a Cornish granite base at British Aerospace's Brooklands site. At this time Aerostructures Hamble was gearing itself up for future growth in the aerospace business. In February 1990 it commissioned a new MRP II manufacturing control system which represented a £1.7million investment in hardware, software and personnel training. This big investment was an indication of AHL's determination to be the best in the business. John Perry, AHL's managing director said 'What we have got now, in our hands, is a tool of world class standard. Another piece of equipment which we can choose to use properly, helping us to beat the competition, helping to secure our future'.

The following month Aerostructures Hamble announced that it had established Specialised Elastomers, a semi-autonomous unit within the Company. As AHL's products and services in this field have applications across a wide range of industries, this facility was set up to meet customers' demands for individual attention and high levels of service. With a growing portfolio this business area is now part of the TI Group's Speciality Polymer Products division.

A favoured publicity ploy by aircraft industry companies was – and probably still is – the garnering of order stories during the run-up to the SBAC Farnborough Exhibition – then releasing them during the week of the Show when the eyes of the world were focussed on British aviation achievements. AHL wasn't a company to buck the system. To coincide with the September 1990 Exhibition it announced two major orders: the Saab Scania order was for the design and supply of structural components for the Saab 2000 twin-turboprop commuter aircraft. At that time orders and options for 135 Saab 2000s had been received by the Swedish aircraft manufacturer which believed that there was a potential for 300 aircraft sales by the year 2000. The second order, worth $100 million, was from McDonnell Douglas Aircraft Company for sub-assemblies of the wing trailing edge panels and flap fairings for the superb C-17 Globemaster III four-jet, long range, heavy airlifter. This successful aeroplane provides airlift capability from bases in the US directly to basic airfields world-wide. The C-17 programme is of great significance to Aerostructures Hamble as the Company forges ahead into new world markets.

A Harrier T52, ZA250/G-VTOL, and Hawk Mk 50, ZA101/G-HAWK, head for the 1979 Paris Air Show. Each carries the new British Aerospace name on its front fuselage.

Hamble's fifty-seven acres in 1979. Cliff House is visible at the top of the picture with Sydney Lodge's rear elevation seen lower centre.

The new machine shop, under construction at Hamble, was opened by Sir Austin Pearce, British Aerospace Chairman, on 5 October 1982. British Marine Aircraft's original 1935 hangar, now the main assembly hall, is behind it.

Hamble 1982 with new machine shop at top of the slipway, new design complex mid right, plastics facility lower left and the new despatch building far left. This view shows the major additions made since 1979.

Airbus at Farnborough. Hamble manufactures wing leading edge components and sub-assemblies for A300 and A310 variants.

An A310 wing built specially for bird strike damage assessment tests, seen in the main assembly hall.

Saab 340 wing root fairings in the new non-metallic facility during 1983.

Hamble moulded composite inter-fuselage wing fairings for the Saab 340B. Design and manufacture was also undertaken for the Saab 2000, lower left.

Roll-out of the prototype British Aerospace 146 quiet four-jet passenger aeroplane, appropriately registered G-SSSH, at Hatfield on 20 May 1981. Production variants have fuselage spines, fairings and cabin windows built at Hamble.

The British Aerospace Advanced Turboprop airliner, the ATP/Jetstream 61, was fitted with Hamble-built composite engine nacelles and landing gear doors.

Ministry of Supply Gnat F1, XK740, returns to Hamble for refurbishment before being displayed in Southampton's Mitchell Hall of Aviation. This Gnat first flew on 6 March 1957 and was handed over to the Museum on 5 March 1987.

The first prototype YAV-8B, with a new composite material wing structure, takes shape in McDonnell Douglas's St Louis plant. Hamble manufactures full-scale development aircraft rear fuselages and airbrakes for the successful AV-8B programme.

McDonnell Douglas AV-8B full-scale development aircraft. Of interest are the two rows of boundary layer doors on the air intakes. One row was deleted on production aircraft.

97

The Ajeet Mk 2 trainer, designed and developed by Hindustan Aircraft Ltd in India, first flew on 20 September 1982. The programme was suspended for a year, then reinstated but finally abandoned in 1988. Two aircraft were built, E2626 and E2427.

Referred to as the EAP, this aircraft was the technology demonstrator for Britain's Experimental Aircraft Programme. First flying in the Autumn 1986, it was the forerunner of the Eurofighter 2000 Typhoon. Its cockpit canopy, windscreen and spine hatch were Hamble products.

Major fuselage assemblies, empennage and canopies were produced for the Sea Harrier. This first Sea Harrier FRS1, XZ450, at Dunsfold, was first flown at Dunsfold by John Farley on 20 August 1978.

British Aerospace
Sea Harrier FRS1.
Dunsfold installed
all the systems
and equipment in
the Hamble
fuselage
structures.

Farewell Gnat – Hello Hawk! Eight Red Arrows fly an impeccable Concorde formation during their last display with Gnats in 1979. On the ground is the Gnat's successor, a British Aerospace Hawk.

Export Hawks. High over the Swiss Alps this Hawk Mk 66 was one of a number collaboratively built by Swiss Industry, British Aerospace and Rolls-Royce. U-1259 was the eighth assembled in Switzerland.

A significant element of the US Navy Training System, the T45 Goshawk embodies Hamble-manufactured fuselage components, canopy and windscreen assemblies.

Five
New Challenges

While British Aerospace was still shaking down into what it believed would be a longer-lasting configuration, further changes were made. Its January 1989 'packaging' of the Hamble company ready for future sale moved forward a stage on 8 November 1991 when BAe announced that Aerostructures Hamble Ltd was to be sold off. The principal reason was that BAe had now defined its four core business areas and AHL, as a parts and sub-assemblies supplier, was not within them.

In the interim at Hamble while a new buyer was being sought, Boeing recognized that AHL had complied with this giant US company's quality requirements. Thus, in March 1992, it awarded a contract to AHL for sets of wing leading edge ribs for the new Boeing 757 twin-engine airliner.

The sale of the Hamble company was achieved through a management buyout in May of 1992 with the assistance from various financial institutions in the City which provided the venture share capital to fund the purchase. Under this new management the Boeing company awarded AHL its D1-9000 Advanced Quality Systems Approval. This was followed with an order for some 60,000 Boeing 747-400 aircraft detail components for the Boeing Northrop fuselage programme with a second larger contract for wing leading edge components to be supplied in kit form direct to the assembly line for the Boeing 737-700 New Generation twin-jet airliner. Work was also undertaken on Boeing 777 strakelets and composite floor panels. There was a lot of Hamble ingenuity at far away Seattle.

On the European front during this period orders were received from SATIC in Toulouse for the design, tooling and manufacture of the very large 24ft diameter front cargo door, which weighs two tons, and the fixed structure on which it was hung, for the A300-600 Super Airbus Transporter. Working in partnership with the German Dornier company, AHL designed the structure for this door. Tooling and manufacture was all done by AHL and its subcontract partners; moreover, Hamble also designed and installed the associated hydraulic systems for these doors. It also produced the Master Tooling Gauge, a 'dummy' door which was use by Airbus Industrie's Toulouse factory to control the cargo door-to-aircraft interface.

In order to accommodate the door during manufacture, Aerostructures Hamble had to change the structure of the main assembly hall roof, re-route some electrical supply lines and build an enclosure around the entire assembly jig and door to provide a paint spraying facility with its own extraction system.

On 6 December 1993 the first door left AHL's slipway on a barge which took it to Southampton for shipping to Bordeaux from whence it travelled by road to Toulouse. Five doors and fixed structures have been made with the fifth door being handed over on 10 February 2000.

For Eurofighter 2000 extensive qualification and development trials with the supersonic underwing fuel tanks to support the aircraft's development programme were under way in parallel with initial production. Creation of this special tank was a partnership led by AHL, the other partners being CASA in Spain, Germany's DASA and the Italian AEREA company. They are certainly European tanks!

Looking at more traditional production lines, work on Hawks was gathering pace with the introduction of the new Hawk 100 two-seater and the 200 single-seat variants. The Harrier production programme also kicked in with eighteen new-build Sea Harrier FA2 fighter/attack aircraft which gives these Royal Navy aircraft an AMRAAM capability. These new programmes were a challenge to everyone at Hamble.

To enable the new AHL management's pay-back of venture capital to be made and to promote further investment in the Company, on 29 March 1994 the Board announced that it intended to seek a listing of the Company's shares on the London Stock Exchange as Aerostructures Hamble Holdings plc (AHH). This was achieved in June 1994.

In the meantime new factory equipment was being installed and commissioned as Aerostructures Hamble continued its on-going programme to keep on the leading edge of technological capability. A new fluid cell press for the Press Shop, a larger autoclave for the Composites Section and another five-axis machining centre were among these new facilities. These were matched by reorganization of teams of skilled specialised operators. The first half of 1995 saw a number of historic events. The end of a very long-running contract had come in late March with the delivery of the last of 452 BAe Hawk centre and rear fuselages built by the Hamble Company. In May the second fixed structure for the A300-600 Super Airbus Transporter aircraft left Hamble and the second main cargo door followed it to Toulouse in June.

In the interim period however, in such a volatile economic climate, AHH plc was very vulnerable to market fluctuations and at a time when its value was at a low ebb it was bought up by EIS plc. The announcement of this acquisition was made on 2 November 1995, Aerostructures Hamble Holdings having published only one set of accounts as a public limited company.

An impressive sight. A Boeing C-17 Globemaster III heavy-lift aircraft takes off showing all eight of its large flap hinge fairings behind its wings.

Pictured at Dunsfold in early 1999 are the last Hawker P1127, XP984 (left) and the last British Aerospace Sea Harrier FA2, ZH813.

Dressed to impress. ZJ100, the Hawk 100 demonstrator and test aircraft shows off its canopy and windscreen.

The second pre-production single-seat Hawk, ZH200, just milliseconds from touchdown on Dunsfold's runway. Development of its transparencies was undertaken at Hamble.

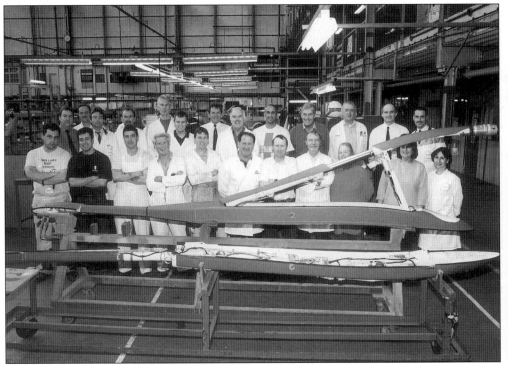

The retractable flight refuelling probe for the Tornado IDS variant with the Hamble team which produced it. This was the last one of Batch 9 in April 1998.

Four types of RAF aircraft, all of which rely on Hamble Group products, engage in an in-flight refuelling exercise. The big VC10K3 tanker leads, from left, a Eurofighter Typhoon, ZH588, plus two Tornado F3s and a SEPECAT Jaguar.

Aerostructures produced inboard flap assemblies with vanes, including wing flex joints for both Boeing MD80 and MD90 programmes. Repairs and spares continue to be supplied today.

This successful 'bizjet', the Raytheon 125, has its tailplane, fin and rudder and overfin manufactured at Hamble.

Three of the Avroliner family of regional jets. Hamble-built components include the fuselage spines, fairings and cabin windows.

Sino Swearingen SJ30-2 engine nacelle on final assembly.

Engineers work on the fixed structure for the A300-600 Beluga. Here it is being prepared for transporting to Toulouse.

The first nose cargo door for the Beluga is moved out of its construction jig. The hangar door and slipway, built by British Marine Aircraft almost sixty years earlier, are used for its despatch.

The Beluga takes shape with the cargo door being fitted in the Toulouse factory.

Old meets New. The A300-600 Beluga has replaced the Super Guppy which, for some twenty-five years, carried large Airbus components from various European partners' factories to the final assembly sites. With a 350mph top speed the Beluga is almost twice as fast its predecessor and carries twice the payload at over forty-five tons.

The SATIC A300-600 Beluga Number 3. By October 2000 five aircraft had been built.

Hamble Aerostructures supply composite floor sections to the Boeing 777 production line.

Having been on Boeing's New Generation 737 programme from its inception, Hamble supplies wing leading edge metallic and composite components and sub-assemblies direct to the Boeing assembly line for this growing family of aircraft.

Six

C. F. Taylor, Beagle and EIS

The question everyone was asking at the time of the 1995 takeover was 'Who are EIS?'. (Electrical and Industrial Securities). The answer and the background to this acquisition are lengthy and complex. Briefly, back in 1951 Cyril F. Taylor had formed a small but very successful sheet-metal working company named C.F. Taylor (Metalworkers) Ltd. Its early growth in the 'tin bashing' business was almost entirely in aviation work. In collaboration with a partner small workshops in Reading and Crowthorne were set up to undertake urgently required work from Bristol Aeroplane Co. at Filton and Vickers Armstrong Aircraft Co. at Weybridge. As this type of sub-contract work grew rapidly, a new site in Molly Millar's Lane at Wokingham was acquired. Within three years this Group was seeking premises in the Bournemouth area which could target the de Havilland company at Somerford and Vickers at Hurn for sub-contract work. Some Ministry of Supply buildings were leased at Hurn in 1955 and a precision engineering branch, C.F. Taylor (Hurn) was established there. However, within twelve months, these premises proved inadequate to cope with the volume of work and a site at Stony Lane was bought for less than £6,000. There the Christchurch factory rose out of the water meadows, a facility which has been steadily expanded ever since.

In 1961 C.F. Taylor (Holdings) Ltd was formed. During the ensuing six years it grew into a group of thirteen companies, five of which formed the Aircraft Division. During December of that year the Weir Group, which was a Glasgow-based engineering business, acquired a controlling interest in CFT (Holdings) Ltd.

Meanwhile, British Executive Aircraft and General Light Engineering Ltd (Beagle) at Shoreham Airport was struggling to launch a new range of light aircraft in a highly competitive market on which the US Piper, Beech and Cessna companies had established a strangle-hold. Beagle had been founded in 1960 by Peter (later Sir Peter) Masefield with financial backing from the giant Pressed Steel company. Masefield had left the Bristol Aeroplane Co. taking with him the design and manufacturing rights to the Bristol Types 219 and 220, five-seat single and twin-engine business aircraft respectively. The Type 220 was to become the basis of the Beagle 206 variants among which was the Basset, of which twenty were built for the RAF. With the acquisition of the Auster and the Miles Aircraft companies, the range of Beagle designs widened to include a single-engine, side-by-side, two-seat trainer/sport aircraft named the Pup which first flew on 8 April 1967.

But the Beagle company was in deep financial trouble. To keep it afloat, in July 1968 it was formally taken over as a wholly Government-owned company. Hopes for success rose when the Bulldog, a Pup military variant, flew on 19 May 1969 but, before any could be completed, Beagle went into receivership following the withdrawal of further Government support. Beagle Aircraft (1969) Ltd was set up to continue day-to-day business until a buyer could be found. On 27 February 1970 Cork Gulley were appointed Receivers and in June Scottish Aviation Ltd took over the manufacture and development of the Bulldog.

While Beagle had been encountering the beginnings of its death throes, in January 1967 C.F. Taylor (Holdings) had became a wholly-owned subsidiary of the Weir Group but retained its operating autonomy. Thus, in 1970, it formed an Associate company with Scottish Aviation Ltd named Dart Herald (Support) Ltd. This took over ownership and supply of parts for Dart-powered Herald short-haul transports from Handley Page Aircraft Ltd which also had gone into liquidation.

Meanwhile, Beagle Aircraft (1969) at Shoreham was no longer making aircraft but had continued the sub-contract manufacture of major aircraft structures. On 4 January 1971 CFT (Holdings) made an £80,000 offer to the Receivers for Beagle's sub-contract manufacturing business. This was accepted free of all liabilities. Then the company's lease on the factory was terminated and it was given three months notice to quit the airfield which was owned by the Shoreham Council. All capital equipment such as jigs, tooling and materials were moved to Christchurch within four months and to facilitate a smooth transaction the name Beagle Aircraft (1969) Ltd was transferred to the C.F. Taylor (Hurn) company which ran the new acquisition as a subsidiary. A new building was erected to house it.

At that time the Beagle order book was worth £300,000, principally for Rolls-Royce Spey engine cowlings for de Havilland Trident and BAC One Eleven airliners plus external stores pylons for the Jaguars which were being built by British Aircraft Corporation at Warton, Lancs. Rolls-Royce Quality Control approved the transfer of contracts and BAC had already approved CFT (Hurn). When production of 150 Bulldogs for the RAF was completed at Scottish Aviation's Prestwick, Ayrshire, plant, the Christchurch factory built sub-assemblies for this aircraft's control surfaces and engine cowlings; moreover it became the preferred supplier for product support. Ultimately, 325 Bulldogs were built. Contract work then expanded and prime customers included Boeing, British Aerospace, Rolls-Royce and Shorts. Other work undertaken included the manufacture of flight simulator cockpit shell structures. In 1988 the trading name then reverted to Beagle Aircraft Ltd and C.F. Taylor (Hurn) slipped quietly into history.

It was in January 1978 that EIS plc entered the picture. In a near £1.5 million deal, the ownership of C.F. Taylor (Holdings) Ltd was then transferred from the Weir Group to EIS. This company had been formed in 1899 as the English Velvet and Cord Dyers Association. Based in Manchester it was primarily involved with the Lancashire cotton industry. During the Second World War the Government ordered it to stop making velvet and produce khaki cloth for uniforms. At the war's end when Britain's textile industry virtually collapsed as the market was flooded by cheap imports of cotton goods from the Far East, it had no central role; so, in 1959, the company diversified into an industrial holding company named E.V. Industrials. With its acquisition of CFT (Holdings) it widened its already diverse interests, its Aircraft and Precision Engineering Division having twelve companies with 2,500 employees. EIS continued an already established policy of concentrating on niche markets for aircraft galley equipment, sub-contract manufacture of airframe sub-assemblies and components, metal and plastic-bonded panels and a range of filters, valves and pumps. As this book was published the Beagle site at Christchurch was busy producing major aircraft structures and providing product support for Harrier, Tornado and Jaguar aircraft.

For the next three years Aerostructures Hamble was to continue as an important element of EIS of which it was a wholly-owned subsidiary. Customers confirmed their confidence in AHL and saw this change of ownership as being a move to greater stability in the Company. One in particular, McDonnell Douglas in the USA, believed that a recent contract for MD80/90 components would provide work for some five years. Boeing, too, took notice of the on-time deliveries which Hamble regularly achieved. It had been a tough passage but AHL had secured a firm foothold in US markets.

By then in EIS ownership, Hamble did not rest on its laurels. Continued investment in new production facilities included the installation of additional CATIA work stations in various sections of the factory and the modernising of its work practices. There were, too, a number of senior engineering and management changes which strengthened these areas of responsibility and expertise at a significant waypoint in the evolution of the Company. It was not too long before that evolution would reach another even more significant point.

Having previously occupied leased premises C.F. Taylor (Hurn) Ltd moved to a purpose-built plant which rose up from the water meadows at Christchurch. It was from here that the factory expanded to meet the increasing work load of new contracts.

C.F. Taylor manufactured a range of aircraft equipment including these mobile steps for passenger access to aircraft. The steps to this prototype Avro 748 were photographed on 7 September 1960 at the SBAC's Farnborough Exhibition.

C.F. Taylor (Hurn) and Beagle (1969) received orders for Rolls-Royce Spey engine cowlings for the BAC One Eleven airliner. Manufacture continued until 1984. 'Hush kits' were then made to meet the latest international noise regulations.

C.F. Taylor (Hurn) manufactured considerable numbers of these huge fillet flaps for the Boeing E3 AWACS programme. First orders were received in 1978.

ZH101, a Boeing E3 Sentry AEW Mk 1 of No.8 Squadron, Royal Air Force carries its 'rotodome' rotating radar antenna on its back.

This shiny example of the metal-worker's skill is the lower engine cowling for the Short 360 short-haul passenger aircraft.

The Pratt & Whitney Canada PT6A turboprop engines in this US Army Short C-23A Sherpa transport, a military version of the 360, also have cowlings made at Christchurch.

115

Sepecat Jaguar tailplanes at Beagle Aircraft's plant for overhaul. They are one of many of this aircraft's components which are repaired on site to keep the Jaguar in RAF front-line service.

With its Adour engines' reheat wicks turned right up, this Jaguar GR1, XZ113, gets airborne in dramatic style. The Jaguar programme has been very significant for Beagle Aircraft as it has provided work for over twenty-five years.

Close-up view of a Royal Navy Sea Harrier FA2 for which Beagle Aircraft is a prime manufacturer of spares components. It is anticipated that the Sea Harrier will remain in service until about 2015.

Seven

Closed Circle

This significant point in AHL's evolution was the acquisition of EIS by the giant TI Group in July 1998 which was an important milestone for the Hamble company. TI Group's mission statement, or strategy, is to be an international engineering group concentrating on specialised engineering businesses, operating in selected niches on a global basis. Key businesses must be able to command positions of sustainable technological and market share leadership. They will have a high knowledge and service content and will be able to anticipate and meet customers' needs.

Currently, TI Group has four world leading business groups. One of these is Dowty, a well established leader in specialised aerospace systems for major civil and military aircraft programmes throughout the world for which it provides a range of aerospace and defence products and services. Aerostructures Hamble met the criteria highlighted in TI Group's mission statement and became part of the Dowty Group of companies.

In this way Aerostructures Hamble has come full circle. How so? In 1924 Henry Folland, who was then Chief Designer of Gloster Aircraft Co., persuaded a young design draughtsman to leave his board in A.V. Roe's design office at Hamble and move to Gloucestershire. The young man's name was George Dowty. In 1931 he founded Aircraft Components Company which was the foundation on which the Dowty Group was based. Sixty-one years later, when the TI Group acquired it, Dowty was an international group of some seventy companies with disparate products ranging over equipment for aircraft and aero-engines and for the mining, bulk handling, machine tool, industrial hydraulic, electric and electronic, communications and polymer industries.

Under the Dowty banner, Aerostructures Hamble has advanced its expertise in creating high quality products to meet strict delivery dates at contract-winning prices with an ongoing focus on Lean Manufacturing techniques. The Company heads into the twenty-first century with a full portfolio of civil and military products. Among them are Airbus A340-500/600 wing trailing edges, Airbus 300/310 and Boeing 737-700 wing leading edges, Raytheon Hawker 125 tail units, Sino Swearingen SJ30-2 engine nacelles, and Avro RJ spines and fairings.

Military programmes being supplied include Boeing C-17 Globemaster III flap hinge fairings, wing trailing edge panels and fuel jettison islands, Tornado mid-life update structural kits and canopies, Eurofighter 2000 in-flight refuelling probes, and 1,000 litre supersonic drop tanks, Harrier II wing leading edge root extensions (LERX), Hawk and Goshawk T45 windscreens and canopies, role equipment, weapon pylons, centre-line fuel tanks and major structural sub-assemblies.

At the time this book went to press, another chapter is already opening regarding Hamble's history. In October 2000 TI Group announced a proposed merger with Smiths Industries Plc. The shareholders of both groups voted on 17 November 2000, and Aerostructures Hamble is now part of Smiths Group.

The history books have it that Hamble-le-Rice saw Saxon invaders land here in 495AD followed by Jutes twenty years later. They record that the great longboats of the Danes crunched into the foreshore here to disgorge horn-helmeted pirates who laid waste the area. No doubt in 1936 local residents raised their voices against the erection of a giant hangar on the Yorke family lands. But this great building and others which now surround it have played a full part in creating the 'tools' for our defences in war and peace and for the development of air travel. Today Aerostructures Hamble is an integral part of Hamble-le-Rice and it must not be forgotten that the Company has provided employment for many thousands of Hampshire people. Long may it continue so to do.

The Circle. George Dowty's first landing gear design gets airborne on this Aldershot bomber designed and built by A.V. Roe and Co. which, in 1916, had built a factory and established an airfield to the east of British Marine Aircraft's site at Hamble. In 1924 Henry Folland employed Dowty at Gloster Aircraft Co. which was designing fighters like the Gamecock, Gauntlet and Gladiator. There was no crystal ball to foretell the return of the Dowty name to Hamble nearly seventy-five years later.

This impressive two-ton Hamble-built A300-600 Beluga cargo door is operated by internally-locking Dowty hydraulic actuators which allow loading of this A340-600 wing assembly.

Eight

Project File

Although only three basic types of aircraft were produced by Folland Aircraft, the Fo108 flying test bed, the Midge and the Gnat, a substantial number of projects emanated from the Folland design office. Project numbers ran from Fo100 to Fo148 the details of most have been traced. Project numbers were not given to a 1939 four-engine, transatlantic monoplane to Specification 14/38, to which Short Bros and Miles Aircraft responded, or to a medium range airliner to Specification 15/38 of the same year which brought responses from the Fairey Aviation and General Aircraft companies.

Fo100 Believed to have been a single-engine, Rolls-Royce Vulture-powered bomber. April 1937.

F0100A Single-engine bomber with same engine as F0100. August 1937.

F0101 Twin-engine fighter with Alvis Pelides engines. April 1937.

F0102 Interceptor fighter powered by Rolls-Royce Vulture engine. April 1937.

F0103 No details known.

Fo104 Twin-engine torpedo-spotter/reconnaiscance aircraft with Aquila engines. July 1937.

Fo105 Twin-engine, medium civil transport powered by Napier Rapier engines. November 1937.

Fo106 Twin-engine, medium civil transport possibly to specification C.15/38 with Aquila engines. November 1937.

Fo106A Four-engine, medium civil transport to either C.14/38 or C.15/38 with Bristol Taurus engines August 1938.

Fo107 Interceptor fighter powered by Napier Sabre engine. April 1938.

Fo108 Flying engine test bed to Specification 43/47 of which twelve were built. Known almost universally as the Folland Frightful ! July 1938.

Fo109 A single seat, twin-Cyclone engine photographic aircraft. October 1939.

Fo110 A twin seat version of the F109. October 1939.

Fo111 A 1939/40 single engine bomber. November 1939.

Fo111A Single-engine bomber with Twin Wasp engine. January 1940.

Fo112 1940 single engine unarmed bomber with Wasp or Sabre engines. January 1940.

Fo112A Single-engine unarmed bomber with Sabre engines. September 1940.

Fo113 Twin engined two seat bomber to specification B1/40.

Fo114 As F113 but with Rolls-Royce Griffon engines

Fo115 A 1940 Napier Sabre-engined torpedo/reconnaissance bomber to Specification E28/40.

Fo116 As above with a variable-incidence wing and a 2,400hp Bristol Centaurus engine.

Fo116A As above with Centaurus III engine. March 1942.

Fo117 A single-seat fighter to Specification F6/42 with a 2,400hp Centaurus engine. It was planned for production by another company as an 'insurance' fighter in the event that the Gloster F9/40 Meteor jet fighter was a failure. September 1942.

Fo117A A revised Fo117 to Specification F19/43 with a laminar flow wing and a 2,500hp Centaurus engine. A single-jet engine variant had no project number. December 1943.

Fo118 A 1943 single-seat Naval fighter to Specification N.7/43 with Centaurus engine. May 1943.

Fo119 A 1943 single-engine dive bomber to Specification O.5/43. June 1943.

Fo120 A 1944 twin-engine amphibian with Aquila or Leonides engines. October 1844.

Fo121 A 1945 Air Observation Post aircraft to Specification A4/45 with a 250hp de Havilland Gipsy Queen 31 engine. March 1945.

Fo121A Light communications AOP aircraft to Specification A4/55. DH Gipsy Queen 31 engine. March 1945.

Fo121C The same design but with DH Gipsy Queen 51 engine fitted. March 1945.

FO121E The same design but with a DH Gipsy Queen 71 engine fitted. March 1945.

Fo122 Five-seat personnel aircraft with Gipsy Queen 71 engine. March 1946.

Fo123 Twin-engine tail-less amphibian with DH Gipsy Queen 71 engines.

FO124 Two/three-seat trainer powered by Lycoming or Cirrus Minor engines. June 1946.

Fo125 Single-engine amphibian with Gipsy Queen 31 engines.

Fo126 A 1946 Rolls-Royce Griffon-powered private venture, air-sea-rescue amphibian. September 1946.

Fo127 A light passenger/cargo aircraft, named the Fiona, with three 145hp Gipsy Major engines. September 1946.

Fo128 An all-metal troop-carrying glider to Specification X30/46. March 1947.

Fo129 A 1947 "Fiona" eight seat personnel aircraft with three Gipsy Queen engines. April 1947.

Fo130/01 Six/eight-seat civil transport with three Cirrus Major III engines. November 1947.

Fo130/02 Eight-seat civil transport with same engines as above. March 1948.

Fo130/03 Five/eight-seat civil transport with two Armstrong Siddeley Cheetah 25 engines. March 1948.

Fo130/04 Eight/ten-seat civil transport as above. March 1948.

Fo131 A wooden Fo128 glider.Proposed July 1948.

Fo132 Single-engine trainer to Specification T.16/48 with Cheetah 10 engine. February 1949.

Fo133. Research for RAE Farnborough. March 1949.

Fo134 A joint 1948-1949 project with Saunders-Roe for an eleven passenger feeder-liner to Specification 26/49 as a DH Rapide replacement. Saunders-Roe designated it the P132. Four 145hp DH Gipsy Major or four 180hp Blackburn Bombardier engines. A second variant for seventeen passengers had four Gipsy Queen II engines. October 1949.

Fo135 Plastics research for RAE Farnborough. February 1949.

Fo136 Aero-generation research for ERA.

Fo137 Aero-generation research for Ministry of Fuel and Power.

Fo138 research for RAE. January 1951.

Fo139 The private venture Midge design of 1954 with one 1,650lb thrust Armstrong Siddeley Viper 101 turbojet. One built G-39-1.

Fo140 /1 Lightweight fighter with a 3,750lb thrust Bristol BE22 Saturn turbojet. January 1952.

Fo140/2 The Fo140/1 with a Rolls-Royce Derwent turbojet.

Fo141 The private venture Gnat F1 project powered by a 3,205lb thrust Bristol Orpheus BOr1 turbojet. One built G-39-2.

Fo142 Jet deflection aircraft. October 1953.

Fo143 A development of the Gnat Mk 1, the Mk 2 variants included a trainer, a two-seat night-fighter, a navalised Gnat and a single seat fighter. The essential differences between the Mk 1 and Mk 2 were a 6% thickness/chord ratio wing instead of the 8% wing and an Orpheus engine with reheat to produce a level supersonic performance. These studies were made between 1959 and 1961.

Fo144 The Gnat T1 two-seat trainer of 1959 powered by one 4,400lb thrust Orpheus BOr 4/101. Built to meet Ministry of Aviation Specification T185D/P. First aircraft XM691. This led to further development of the trainer programme with basic all-through and advanced Gnat studies. Span 24ft length 31ft 9in.

This Folland project designation also possibly covered two Gnat derivatives during 1959-1963. The Gnat Mk 4, a further developed Mk 2 with a 6% thickness/chord ratio wing having more extensive slats and flaps and powered with a single unspecified reheated engine, and the Gnat Mk 5 trainer and interceptor fighter with two Rolls-Royce RB 153 reheated turbojet engines. Span was 24ft, length 38ft and wing area was 170 sq ft.

Fo145 Twin engined V.T.O. aircraft of January 1958

Fo146 Design based on the Gnat Mk 5 but having variable geometry to meet the changing training requirements and to test effective solutions leading to higher performance front line aircraft. Length 41ft, span at 20 degrees sweep 34ft 2in and 21ft at 65° sweep. Slats and flaps fitted.

Fo147 Variable geometry wing with 0-25 º sweep angle where maximum use to be made of high-lift devices, and with a 60-70 º sweep for Mach 2.0 plus performance. Powered by two side-by-side fuselage-mounted reheated RB 153 turbojets. Two variants were investigated, one tailless with a retractable foreplane, the other with a conventional tail unit and modified wingtips.

Fo148 An advanced two-seat variable geometry trainer. One reheated RB153-61 turbojet with an optional thrust reverser. Intended as a replacement for the Gnat trainer but with more potential for weapon carriage. Length 47ft, span at 20 º sweep 35ft and 22ft 9in at 65 ºsweep.

HS1170B Though carrying a Hawker Siddeley Aviation designation, the original design revealed its Folland pedigree. Vectored-thrust aircraft to Specification AST.326 with BS94/5 engine. May 1964.

HS1171 Proposed in October 1964 and considered for advanced trainer and light strike roles with variants of two RB172 turbojet engines. To meet Specification AST 326. The original design, with variable sweep wings, also revealed its Folland pedigree.

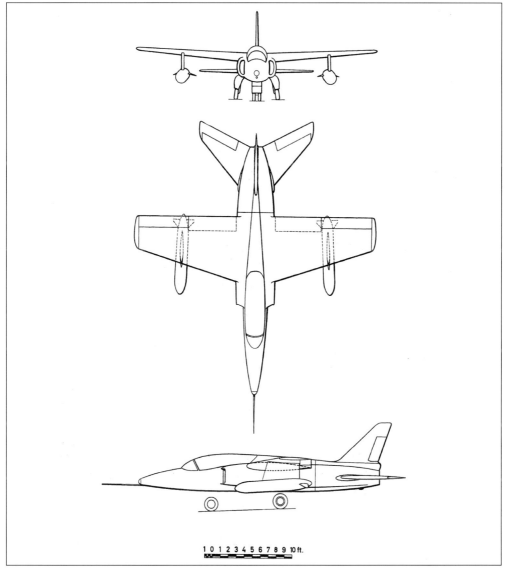

1 0 1 2 3 4 5 6 7 8 9 10 ft.

General Arrangement of Gnat All-through Trainer.

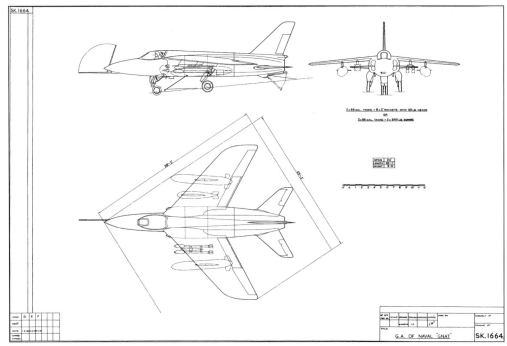

General Arrangement of Naval Gnat.

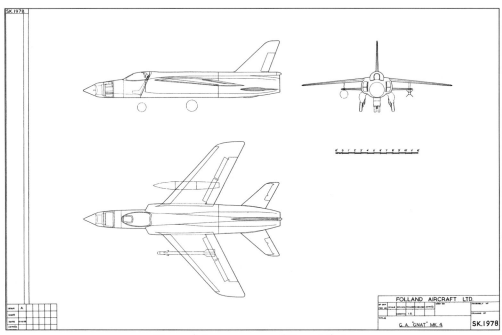

General Arrangement of Gnat Mk 4.

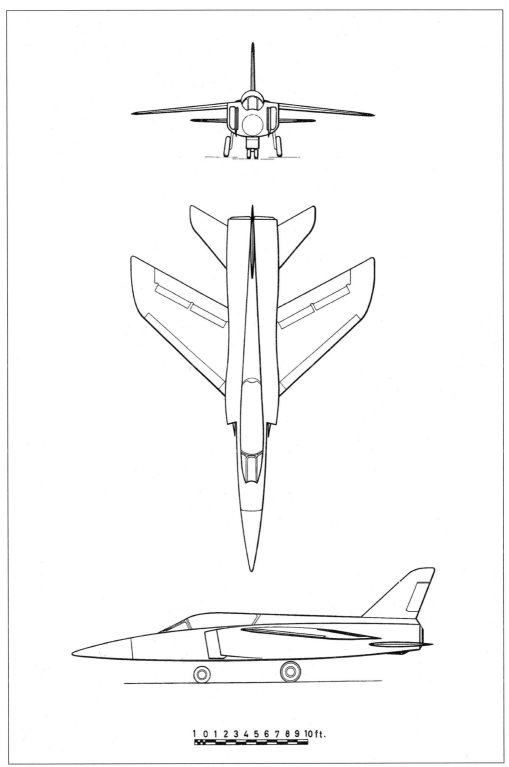

1 0 1 2 3 4 5 6 7 8 9 10 ft.

General Arrangement of Gnat Mk 5.

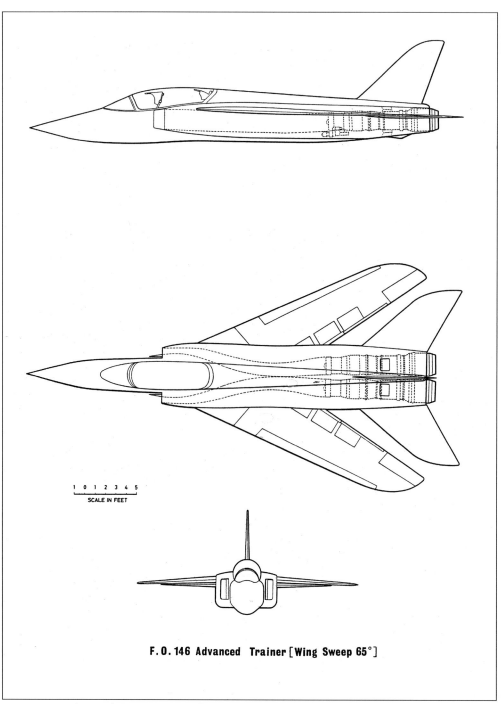

1 0 1 2 3 4 5
SCALE IN FEET

F.O. 146 Advanced Trainer [Wing Sweep 65°]

General Arrangement of Fo146 Advanced Trainer, wing sweep 65°

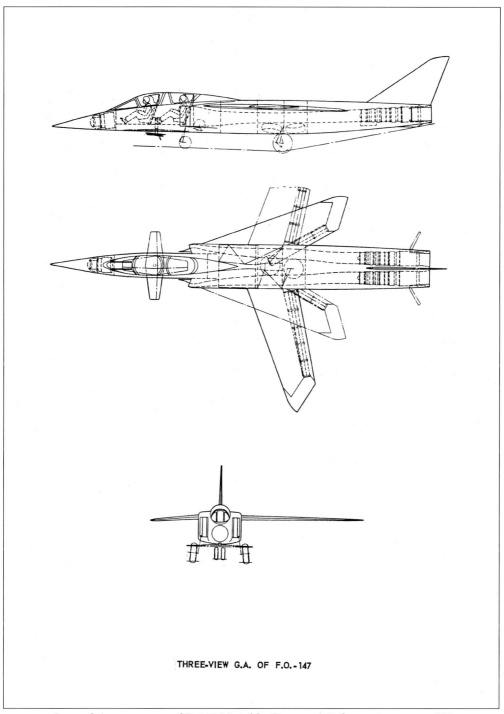

THREE-VIEW G.A. OF F.O.-147

General Arrangement of Fo147 Variable Geometry Fighter, wing sweep 65º

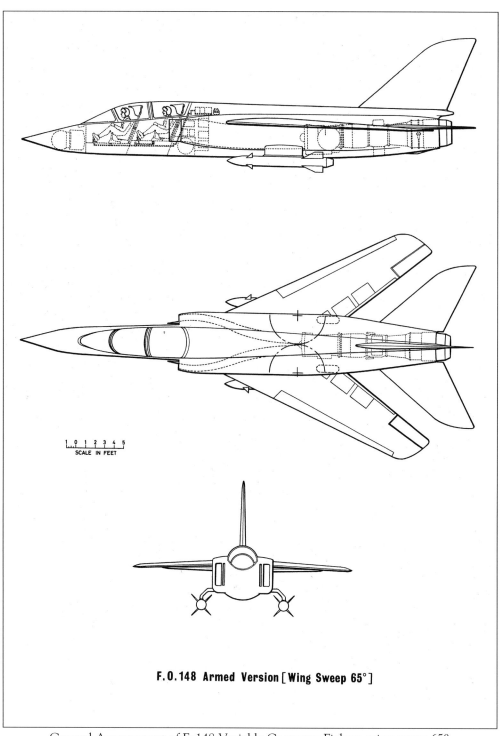

0 1 2 3 4 5
SCALE IN FEET

F.O.148 Armed Version [Wing Sweep 65°]

General Arrangement of Fo148 Variable Geometry Fighter, wing sweep 65°

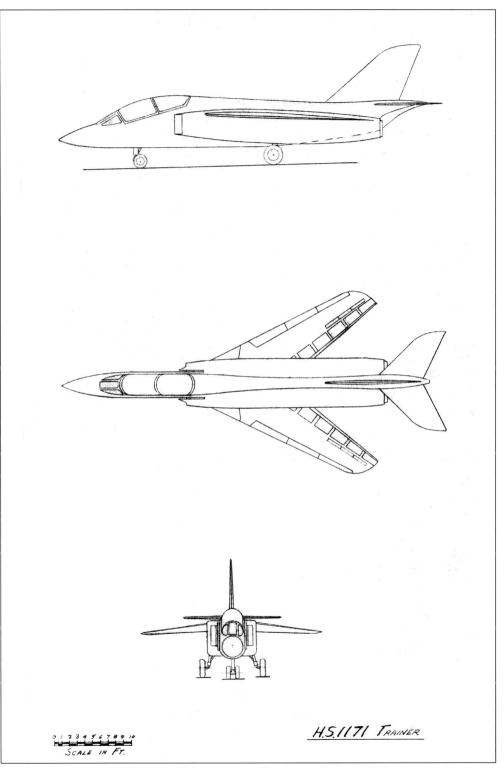

SCALE IN FT.
0 1 2 3 4 5 6 7 8 9 10

H.S.1171 TRAINER

HS1171 Variable Geometry Trainer, wing sweep 65º

Acknowledgements

'No man is an Iland, intire of it selfe' wrote John Donne in the eighteenth century. No author can write a book without the help of others in this twenty-first century. This book would not be in your hands had not friends provided this author with help of many kinds. Chief among them is Chris Hodson, Business Manager – Military of Aerostructures Hamble Ltd who has spent countless hours finding almost all of the photographs, providing detailed information about the Company and its various forebears and whose enthusiasm for the project has been the mainspring which has driven our partnership throughout this year.

The initial inspiration and continued support from Michael Steel, Managing Director Hamble Group, has enabled this remarkable history to be recorded.

I am much indebted to Mike Stroud, who first put my name forward as the author, and to Mike Hooks whose storehouse of photographs and knowledge of aviation history has again come to my aid. Phil Boyden and Gordon Bartley of BAE SYSTEMS contributed photographs and Ken Stone, one-time Managing Director of Beagle Aircraft, assisted with historical facts about that company. Aerostructures Hamble also acknowledges with gratitude the assistance rendered by the Boeing Company, Airbus Industrie, BAE SYSTEMS and Southampton University to this project. As always, my wife Brenda has corrected the spelling and syntax before allowing me to commit these 23,585 words to the little floppy disc.

DNJ,
Barnwood,
Gloucester,
October 2000.